Thermoplastics

Thermoplastics

Properties and Design

A Collective Work Produced by

**Imperial Chemical Industries Limited,
Plastics Division**

Edited by

R. M. Ogorkiewicz
M.Sc. (Eng.), A.C.G.I., D.I.C., C. Eng.,
F.I. Mech. E., F.P.I.

A Wiley–Interscience Publication

JOHN WILEY & SONS
London · New York · Sydney · Toronto

Library of Congress Cataloging in Publication Data:
Main entry under title:
Thermoplastics: properties and design.

"A Wiley-Interscience publication."
Includes bibliographical references.
1. Thermoplastics. I. Ogorkiewicz, Richard M., ed. II.
Imperial Chemical Industries, Ltd. Plastics Division.
III. Title.

TA455.P5T48   620.1'923   73–10742
ISBN 0 471 65306 3

Printed in Great Britain by William Clowes & Sons Limited
London, Colchester and Beccles.

Foreword

That there is a growing use of plastics in applications that demand careful design is undeniable; that this growth rate is as high as the intrinsic nature of plastics warrants is questionable. A major cause of limited exploitation is lack of confidence, the confidence that designers need to have in the capabilities and limitations of plastics as a class of materials, in their interpretation of design data and in their selection of the most suitable type and grade.

A major source of design data is the raw material manufacturer and of recent years there has been a massive, and perhaps sometimes bewildering, output. Data alone, however, are not enough. They often inspire in the users only the unwarranted confidence of those blinded by science. We believe not only that a clear understanding of the properties of plastics is essential to ensure that design data are relevant, but also that this understanding must be backed up by knowledge of how to apply these data to resolve problems in a cost-effective manner.

This book sets out to provide an understanding of the principles underlying the properties of plastics, and also of the design problems associated with plastics in a way that will, I believe, appeal to designers and engineers. The many practical illustrations are taken largely from that range of plastics with which the authors are most familiar.

C. VOWLES
Chairman, ICI Plastics Division

v

Preface

The object of this book is to provide a general understanding of the properties of thermoplastics, to show methods of characterizing them and to indicate how the data which are now becoming available can be used in the design of thermoplastics articles. Of the various properties considered in the book, the mechanical ones are given most attention, because they govern more frequently than others the more exacting applications of thermoplastics. Attention is further centred on the type of information which is available, or required, about the mechanical, as well as other, properties of thermoplastics, rather than the data themselves.

A comprehensive body of data on a representative range of thermoplastics has in fact already been published under the title *Engineering Properties of Thermoplastics*. This collective work was produced by much the same team as that which prepared the current book and I had the privilege of editing it, as well as contributing to it, as I have had of editing the present one. The reception accorded to it encouraged further work on the subject but it was not considered appropriate to produce a second book along the same lines as the first. Reasons for this included the fact that significant advances had taken place in the general understanding of the properties and applications of thermoplastics. Moreover, although a considerable amount of additional information has been produced, it was still not sufficiently complete to warrant the preparation of another book centred on data. It was decided, therefore, to cover, in more general terms, progress made over the whole field of work on the properties of thermoplastics related to design.

As a result, the present work consists of twelve chapters, the first two of which provide a broad background to the use of thermoplastics and a general introduction to their properties. The following nine chapters describe the current state of knowledge of the different facets of the mechanical and other characteristics of thermoplastics. Thus, they cover, one by one, deformational behaviour, long-term durability, short-term strength and impact behaviour, various factors affecting mechanical properties, electrical, thermal and various other physical and chemical properties as well as processing properties and methods. The last chapter describes the use of mechanical design data and presents a number of case studies.

The author, or authors, of each chapter are specialists in the subject or have been closely connected with it. Each chapter contains illustrations of the way in which the different properties of thermoplastics can be characterized or of the way in which data on them can be put to practical, design purposes. Each chapter also includes a list of references or a list of publications recommended for further reading.

London 1973

R. M. OGORKIEWICZ

Contents

5   **Short-term Strength and Impact Behaviour**

P. I. VINCENT, M.A.

6   **Other Factors Affecting Mechanical Properties**

P. I. VINCENT, M.A.

7   **Electrical Properties**

K. A. BUCKINGHAM

8   **Thermal Properties**

A. W. BIRLEY, M.A., D.PHIL., F.P.I., and
D. C. F. COUZENS, B.SC., PH.D.

Contents

1

Introduction

by P. C. Powell

1.1 GENERAL

In contrast with the appreciation of ferrous metals, glass and wood as engineering materials, the appreciation of even the established plastics is less well developed. This book seeks to improve that appreciation by providing some knowledge of the structure and properties of plastics, and by discussing the presentation of design data and ways of using these data to predict the performance of plastics products in service. The purpose of this chapter is to present a broad review of the plastics scene, by discussing the general attributes of plastics, how these materials are processed into products, and where these products are used in engineering and other applications. It is hoped that this will provide some perspective to the detailed discussions presented later in the book.

1.1.1 Attributes and Forms

Many different types of plastics are used to make articles of many varied shapes which fulfil functional requirements in a cost-effective manner. There are four basic features which make plastics of direct interest to designers, engineers and students of materials.

(1) The basic physical properties of plastics can be exploited in a wide range of properly designed articles which have the stiffness, toughness and resilience to resist the loads and deformations imposed during normal use.

(2) Plastics can be made which exhibit a variety of particular properties depending on the type of molecular structure in the material. These properties include transparency, low dielectric loss, low permeability to vapours and extreme chemical inertness.

(3) The shape possibilities for plastics articles are extremely wide, ranging from textile fibres (which are outside the scope of this book) through films and coatings to the three-dimensional articles, often of complicated shape, with which this book is mainly concerned.

(4) Finally, plastics can be readily made into products of complicated shape with repeatable dimensions, using efficient mass production techniques which can result in low unit labour changes.

It is a direct consequence of these attributes and forms that there has been a considerable emphasis on the use of plastics to replace existing materials.

More than twenty different plastics are manufactured in commercial quantities. They may be divided into two distinct and important groups: thermoplastics and thermosetting materials. Thermoplastics, which include acrylic, ABS (acrylonitrile butadiene styrene), nylon, polyethylene, polystyrene and PVC (polyvinyl chloride), account for about three-quarters of the annual production of plastics in the U.K. Thermoplastics are normally more flexible and creep rather more than the thermoset materials. Thermoplastics melt to become viscous liquids each time they are heated, and solidify on cooling: in theory this cycle of softening and hardening can be repeated indefinitely. The stability of the thermoplastic in the molten state confers versatility in a wide range of processing operations and the economics of using rework can be considerable. In contrast, a thermosetting material can only be heated and shaped once, during which process it becomes hard, rigid, insoluble and infusible: it cannot subsequently be reworked and the limited stability of the softened material before curing imposes restrictions on the associated processing techniques. Typical thermosetting materials include phenolics, epoxies and unsaturated polyesters.

1.1.2 Plastics and Engineering

Engineering and engineered applications probably account for as much as a quarter of the current annual production of thermoplastics in the U.K. The range of these applications is wide.

Long runs of pipework are extruded from PVC and from the polyolefins (polyethylene and polypropylene in particular); the largest high-density polyethylene pipes are 1·5 m diameter with 52 mm walls. Liquid storage tanks are being manufactured from acrylic, PVC and polyolefin sheet; one of the largest unsupported tanks, welded from polypropylene sheet, holds 45 m³ and weighs about 2 tonnes empty. Large tanks can also be produced in one piece by other manufacturing methods. Gears range in size from the minute injection-moulded polyacetal precision components used in wrist watches through gears 225 mm pitch circle diameter, 350 mm facewidth and transmitting 50 HP, also injection moulded but in nylon, to the huge 4·25 m diameter, 95 mm facewidth gears monomer cast in nylon. Many motorway bridge bearings, each carrying loads as great as 1000 tonnes, are formed from stainless steel plates which slide over PTFE pads to accommodate movement due to thermal expansion.

There are also load-bearing products engineered from materials, some of which are not usually thought of as 'engineering plastics'. These applications include bottle crates, vegetable trays and other stacking containers injection-moulded from polyolefins; mechanical-handling pallets vacuum-formed from polystyrene and ABS or moulded from polyolefins; and chairs made by a variety of techniques from polypropylene, PVC, ABS, polystyrene, acrylic and polyethylene.

Applications involving critical performance requirements need not, of course, be confined to the realms of mechanical engineering. The use of low-density polyethylene as a dielectric for transatlantic submarine tele-communications cables, and of slot liners made from polyester film to provide electrical insulation and mechanical protection at high running temperatures in the stators of electric motors, are but two examples taken from electrical engineering. However, this book is mainly concerned with thermoplastics in mechanical engineering.

1.1.3 Elements of Design

There are many possible interpretations of the umbrella term 'design'. Certainly one of the tasks of the designer is to ensure that an article will adequately meet service requirements at an acceptable overall cost, and to achieve this the designer must know—from a proper design brief—its purpose. Such a task requires a knowledge and recognition of the strong interactions between such factors as economics, manufacture of raw materials into finished product, properties of materials in end-product form and appropriate selection of materials.

In the early days of the thermoplastics industry the emphasis was on ways of making articles, and factors such as the selection of material and the detailing of product dimensions were almost always relegated to the province of previous experience of similar plastics products and design problems. For many items such an approach is still appropriate today, and the designer draws upon an accumulated wealth of experience: there is after all no need to be erudite for its own sake. Increasingly, however, economic pressures concerning plant investments and product costs dictate a more calculated approach. There is mounting pressure to get the design 'right first time', thus reducing the crippling waste of unnecessary development time, especially in applications where substantial loads have to be carried and where it is essential to use the minimum amount of material commensurate with satisfactory performance.

At this stage a detailed discussion of ways of designing articles is inappropriate. It is more relevant to review the present state of the art in the plastics industry at large, so that the detailed properties of plastics and associated design procedures, to be discussed in the body of this book, can be seen in perspective.

1.2 PLASTICS TECHNOLOGY: EARLY HISTORY AND DEVELOPMENT

1.2.1 Adaptation

It is a feature of the very early days of plastics that the first plastics were closely related to naturally occurring materials, that the delay between chemical discovery and commercial exploitation was great, and that machinery was adapted from existing equipment designed for other classes of materials.

The first thermoplastic, cellulose nitrate, was a horny material produced by digesting wood fibres, paper or rags with nitric acid, and the first items made from this were exhibited in 1862. The chief disadvantage of this material, developed in a plasticized form as 'Celluloid', was its highly inflammable nature. More than half a century was to elapse before a non-flammable variant, cellulose acetate, came into commercial production.

The extrusion process for making spaghetti was known in Italy before 1800: as a discontinuous process it was developed in 1872 to make continuous lengths of rod, bar or sheet from 'Celluloid'. Injection moulding (based on the pressure die casting of metals) was introduced in a crude form in 1878, but both processes were left substantially undeveloped for half a century.

1.2.2 Thermosets

The earliest plastic of real interest to the engineer was the thermosetting resin phenolformaldehyde (PF), introduced as 'Bakelite' in 1907. Uses of PF, processed by compression moulding, were at first restricted to the electrical industry, for making items such as switch bases, terminal blocks, fuse boxes, plugs and sockets. In contrast to the dark opaque colours of PF, aminoplastics based on urea-formaldehyde (UF) introduced in the late 1920s and melamine-formaldehyde (MF) in the early 1930s, offered translucency and a wide range of colours. However, these materials are outside the scope of the book.

1.2.3 Synthesis and Development of Thermoplastics

The modern thermoplastics industry dates from the 1920s when the first processing machinery specifically designed to make articles from thermoplastics on a mass-production scale anticipated the commercial production of materials synthesized from chemical feedstocks rather than from naturally occurring substances.

The first commercial injection moulding machines designed for thermoplastics used injection rams actuated by compressed air. The early 1930s saw the use of pre-plasticization units (in which the plastic was melted before being fed to the injection cylinder) and by the end of the decade shot weights of over a kilogramme had been achieved, using hydraulically operated rams. Machines of more modest capacity were by then already capable of fully automatic operation. In the mid-thirties the early extruders designed for thermoplastics came on to the market.

PVC was in commercial production by the end of the 1920s and in a plasticized form it was replacing rubber for insulating electric cables as early as 1932. Unplasticized PVC, available in 1937, was hard, stiff and tough, and its good chemical resistance was exploited in chemical plant.

The 1930s saw the commercial introduction of three other important thermoplastics: polymethylmethacrylate (acrylic), polystyrene and low-density polyethylene, the first two having natural outstanding transparency. Acrylic first became available in the form of clear, stiff, hard cast sheet which could be readily shaped and which was tougher and safer than glass: it rapidly replaced glass interlayered with cellulose nitrate in aircraft canopies. Acrylic moulding powders also became available in the mid-thirties, albeit in limited quantities. Although polystyrene was cheap, stiff, crystal clear and extremely easy to process, it made an unpromising start because of its extreme brittleness but in a modified form it was later to become an important material. The first polyethylene plant came on stream in 1939. This tough, resilient material found immediate application as an insulant for high-frequency low-voltage cables in radar, and its low-loss properties were later exploited in high-performance transatlantic submarine cables.

Further important materials to be introduced in the 1940s were nylon, ABS and PTFE (polytetrafluoroethylene). The high strength, stiffness and abrasion resistance of nylon were exploited in injection moulded gears and other components which replaced high-quality metal ones in light machinery. The tough ABS materials were introduced in the late 1940s and a toughened, and therefore much improved, 'impact resistant' polystyrene at the beginning of the 1950s. These materials owed much to the earlier synthesis of general purpose rubbers deriving from butadiene and styrene; and the development of the synthetic rubbers stemmed from the need to find a material which was more elastic than plasticized PVC, which was originally used as a natural rubber replacement. PTFE entered commercial production at the end of the 1940s. It is a soft flexible material, chemically inert, an excellent electrical insulator, has outstanding non-stick characteristics and can withstand continuous temperatures in the range $-250°C$ to $+250°C$.

1.3 THE PRESENT RANGE OF MATERIALS AND LIKELY DEVELOPMENTS

1.3.1 The Scale of Operations

In the first twenty years or so of the thermoplastics industry, raw materials derived mainly from coal or from agricultural sources. However, 1950 saw the birth of the modern petrochemical industry, which quickly began to produce in large quantities, and at attractive prices, the basic materials from which most plastics are now made. This was one of the two factors responsible for a tremendous increase in the growth rate of the industry. The other factor was that, at about the same time, understanding of the relationship between molecular structure and the behaviour of plastics became clearer, and recognition of the potential importance of newly developed molecular structures led to rapid commercialization.

At this stage it is helpful to distinguish between two classes of thermoplastics: the low-priced high-tonnage materials (PVC, polyethylene, polystyrene and polypropylene), sometimes called the commodity plastics, and the higher-priced lower-tonnage speciality materials such as acrylic, ABS, PTFE, nylon, polycarbonate, polyacetal, PPO (polyphenylene oxide), polysulphones and thermoplastic polyesters. With the exception of acrylic and ABS, the speciality materials have been developed to offer either a higher modulus or a higher working temperature range, or both, together with other desirable combinations of properties, compared with those afforded by many of the commodity plastics; these attributes usually being achieved at the expense of a higher cost imposed not least by the more humble scale of operations. Such materials have come to be termed 'engineering plastics' but the limitation of this term is that it implies that only the specialist materials are useful within the engineering context, which, as has been mentioned in section 1.1.2, is demonstrably untrue.

1.3.2 The High-Tonnage Materials

At present the U.K. uses more PVC than any other plastic: over 350,000 tonnes in 1971. Compounds can be formulated from PVC and a variety of additives, including plasticizers where appropriate, to cover a remarkably wide range of properties and to be suitable for injection moulding, extrusion, compression moulding and calendering. By virtue of its low cost and the range of grades available, PVC is the most versatile of all plastics. Applications of the unplasticized material (which is self-extinguishing) range from roofing sheet and vandal-proof glazing to pipe fittings, while cable insulation and shoe soling are examples of the use of the more flexible plasticized grades.

Of the 290,000 tonnes of low-density polyethylene used in the U.K. in 1971, much went into applications which exploited toughness, flexibility and chemical resistance to varying degrees. More than 50% of the material is extruded into film, 15% is injection moulded, and about 10% is blow-moulded into bottles and containers. In addition, low-density polyethylene is used in, for example, electrical applications, extruded pipe and rotationally moulded large containers and furniture.

Polystyrene accounted for more than 150,000 tonnes of the plastics used in the U.K. in 1971. There are three basic types: general purpose (G.P.) polystyrene (a rather brittle material), toughened polystyrene and expanded polystyrene. The G.P. type is widely used for toys and the packaging of cosmetics. Toughened polystyrene is used in refrigerator liners, containers for dairy products and housings for domestic electrical equipment, and the expanded form finds application in protective packaging and as a thermal insulating medium.

Polypropylene was introduced in 1959 and its combination of strength, fatigue resistance, stiffness, excellent electrical insulation and temperature and chemical resistance at a low price ensured a phenomenal growth to almost 100,000 tonnes per annum in the U.K. within 12 years. Extruded pipe and sheet are widely used in chemical plant, injection moulded applications (which account for about 50% of the market) include stacking containers and chair shells, and a large number of moulded components are used in cars. Recent developments in its use for twines, fibres, film yarn, carpet backing and face piles have already accounted for 30% of the use of polypropylene, a share which is likely to increase.

High-density polyethylene, introduced in 1954, is much stiffer and stronger than low-density polyethylene, and some of its properties are comparable with those of polypropylene. In 18 years the annual U.K. market has grown to about 60,000 tonnes. About half of the U.K. usage is in blow-moulded containers ranging from small bottles to large tanks, and about 30% in injection moulded items such as dustbins and bottle crates. Sheet and very large pipes are also extruded from high-density polyethylene and currently a rapid growth area is in the use of this material for the replacement of tissue and wrapping paper.

1.3.3 The Specialist Materials

We are concerned here only with a broad picture rather than with an exhaustive treatment. Attention is therefore confined to some of the commercially important materials.

Historically, acrylic is one of the oldest speciality thermoplastics, followed by nylon, ABS and PTFE, all of which were in commercial production by the end of the 1940s. Since then acrylic sheet has almost completely replaced glass for illuminated signs and lighting fittings, and acrylic moulding powders are now the preferred materials for rear-lamp housings for vehicles.

Nylon materials offer good stiffness, strength, toughness and abrasion resistance, but they do absorb moisture which affects their dimensional stability and stiffness. Reinforcement of nylon with glass fibres is widely practised and this increases stiffness and strength, widens the working temperature range and improves the dimensional stability. Normally processed by injection moulding, typical applications include gears, bushes, cams, bearing and housings for power tools and domestic equipment.

ABS, with a stiffness between that of polypropylene and acrylic, has good impact strength and abrasion resistance, but only moderate outdoor weathering resistance. It is used for housings for consumer durables, refrigerator linings, small boat hulls, pipes and fittings, and telephone handsets.

The basic properties of PTFE are described in section 1.2.3. An expensive material, it is used in chemical plant where outstanding chemical resistance is required, as an insulation in high-temperature electrical equipment, in dry and self-lubricating bearings, and as a non-stick coating for cooking utensils.

The late 1950s and 1960s saw the emergence into commercial production of a group of different plastics specifically designed to have a high modulus and high strength, and often (though by no means always) a high upper service temperature. Among the most notable materials in this category are polycarbonate (1958), polyacetals (1959 and 1961), PPO (1964 and 1966), polysulphones (1966 and 1972) and the thermoplastic polyesters (1966). (Where two dates are given, the second refers to the introduction of an important modified material.)

Polycarbonate has outstanding impact strength and is transparent, attributes which are exploited in vandal-proof glazing and street lighting fittings. It is widely used to make machine housings and as a film it is sometimes used as the dielectric of high-performance capacitors.

The excellent resilience of the polyacetals is exploited in light-duty spring applications, and the low coefficient of fraction in gears and bearings. They are used in automotive and plumbing applications and are normally processed by injection moulding.

PPO is tough and has good electrical insulating properties. Injection-moulded applications include hot-water fittings, washing machine components and office machine housings. As film it is used for cable insulation and as a capacitor dielectric. PPO is more widely used when blended with polystyrene, which confers easier processing and a wider range of properties at lower cost.

Polysulphones are used where dimensional and chemical stability at high temperatures is required or where smoke hazards must be avoided, or both. They are used in electrical and electronic equipment and in aircraft ductings.

The thermoplastic polyesters are hard, have good abrasion resistance, and are injection moulded into bushes, bearings, gears and electrical housings. Film (introduced in the early 1950s) is widely used for electrical, packaging, decorative and photographic applications and in the drawing office.

1.3.4 Likely Developments in Materials

The introduction of a completely new plastic has become a rare event. However, there is a continuous process of improvement and modification of existing materials which is often sufficiently dramatic to open up new possibilities in properties, processing techniques and applications. Modifications could include changes in chemical structure, blending of materials to produce 'alloys', changes in particle size and particle size distribution. These, and other changes, could enable materials to be made even more efficiently by the raw materials supplier. Similarly, these changes could result in new grades of existing materials which can be processed more easily, or more rapidly (or both) into finished products.

An important modification in the context of designing load-bearing structures involves the incorporation into a plastics matrix of additives such as short glass fibres, asbestos and talc. The presence of these additives can confer greater strengths and stiffnesses, and improved dimensional stability, and can also modestly extend the upper service temperature, compared with comparable properties of the unfilled material. Particular success has been achieved with optimum proportions of constituents in glass-filled nylon compounds, coupled-glass-reinforced polypropylene and grades of PTFE filled with glass fibre, powdered petroleum coke, graphite and bronze.

Another additive which can confer useful improvements in mechanical properties is a gas; foamed mouldings can be made with a considerable increase in stiffness compared with that for the same weight of unfoamed material. Articles can be produced with a substantially uniform cellular structure throughout, or in the form of a sandwich structure, the solid outer skins conferring particular advantages in flexure.

Likely developments in two other aspects of plastics properties are worth mentioning: they are in weatherability and flammability. A considerable increase in the number of outdoor applications, particularly in the building industry, would result from the manufacture of many types of plastics with improved weatherability. Certainly, more effective stabilizers for particular plastics are continually being devised and this trend in technology will doubtless continue. It will be recognized that another way of improving weatherability is to synthesize materials which are inherently stable to ultraviolet (UV) radiation. Acrylic is outstanding in this respect and other examples are already in small-scale commercial production. A related concept is the judicious combination of materials; e.g. ABS has rather poor UV resistance, but acrylic-capped ABS sheet can be used successfully outdoors because of the excellent resistance of the thin acrylic outer layer.

Thermoplastics are based on a carbon-chain structure, almost all of which can be destroyed by flame or heat. The rate of destruction depends on several factors, notably the nature of the base polymer, the temperature and the duration of the exposure to heat. Polyethylenes generally burn like hard waxes; acrylics burn like hard wood; PTFE and the polysulphones will not burn at all in air at 300°C. It is possible to retard burning by the use of suitable additives, although the presence of these usually has an adverse effect on mechanical properties. Studies are being made of the temperature at which rapid degradation of the thermoplastic into volatile and flammable products takes place. There is, however, little hope of changing the total fuel content in these materials without departing from the basic carbon structure, and this change is at present technically and commercially unattractive.

1.4 THE PRESENT RANGE OF PLASTICS PROCESSING AND FABRICATION TECHNIQUES AND LIKELY DEVELOPMENTS

1.4.1 The Basic Manufacturing Processes

The plastics industry has developed few processing techniques of its own, but has adapted extensively from other technologies. Injection moulding and extrusion were the first processes to be developed specifically for plastics and they are still by far the most important. Extrusion in its various forms accounts for the conversion into semi-finished forms or end products of about 60% of the thermoplastics produced and injection moulding accounts for another 25% or so.

In briefly introducing the other important processes, the dates given in parentheses refer to the generally accepted first decade of commercial use. Thermoforming (1930s) is the plastics counterpart of sheet metal shaping, extrusion blow moulding (1940s) derives from glass blowing, and the sintering of PTFE (1950s) owes much to the technology of powder metallurgy. In contrast, the rotational moulding process (1950s) for producing large hollow articles from thermoplastics powder has no direct parallel in other industries, although in some respects it resembles slush casting. Once techniques of these kinds had become established, substantial advances were made, increasingly rapidly, in the design of machinery for processing plastics, not least in the rates of output which could be achieved and in the size of articles produced. The scale of operations can be judged from the following examples.

Plastics pallets, 1200 mm × 1000 mm × 150 mm, weighing 13 kg, can be injection moulded in one piece at the rate of about 20 units per hour, and other injection mouldings with shot weights of up to 30 kg are in full production. There are also high-speed variants of the process which are capable of producing extremely rapidly comparatively small components to close tolerances at cost savings claimed to be up to 60% over conventional injection moulding methods, provided certain grades of specialist thermoplastics (e.g. nylon 6) are used.

In extrusion, 1·5 m diameter high-density polyethylene pressure pipes are being produced on 150 mm diameter single screw extruders at speeds of about 5 m/h and at a conversion rate of about 1 tonne of raw material per hour. At the other extreme, the extrusion coating of wire with low-density polyethylene commonly involves extrusion speeds of about 100 km/h. Thin film can be made by extruding low-density polyethylene vertically upwards as a thin-walled tube which is subsequently inflated and drawn at a rate exceeding the original extrusion speed: the die for the tube can be 2 m diameter and the circumference of the blown film can already exceed 20 m.

In extrusion blow moulding tanks up to $1 \cdot 1$ m^3 capacity can be made at about 12 units per hour. In contrast milk bottles can be blown using single-head extruders and multi-cavity moulds at rates exceeding one per second.

At present common commercial production of rotational moulding is limited to items of up to about 3 m^3 capacity. Larger specialist items have been produced including tanks weighing up to 540 kg, and a structure $4 \cdot 6$ m $\times$ $4 \cdot 6$ m $\times$ $2 \cdot 4$ m in polyethylene.

The size of equipment for thermoforming plastics sheet has been dominated by the sizes of sheet which have been available. Boat hulls 3 to 4 m long, vacuum formed in ABS, are now established and current product developments reflect the enormous 8 m $\times$ $3 \cdot 5$ m ABS sheets now being used. At the other end of the scale, small thin-walled thermoformed dairy produce containers, e.g. yoghurt pots, are being produced in polystyrene at a rate exceeding 15 m units per annum.

The emphasis in this section so far has been on conventional plastics technology, but this is not to imply that innovation in plastics processing is lacking. An example relates to injection-moulded sandwich structures, in which the surrounding skin can be of a solid thermoplastic and the core of a foamed (and possibly different) thermoplastic: the development of the sandwich-moulding process has been rapid and it can already be used to make thin-walled articles of over $1 \cdot 5$ m^2 projected area and weighing more than 10 kg.

Another example concerns the solid-phase forming (cold forming) of plastics at temperatures below the softening or melting point. The objective is to produce thick-walled parts at high production rates, thus avoiding the penalties of long cooling times associated with their production by injection moulding. This process has suffered delays in development because of the great expense of producing suitable blanks or billets, compared with the cost of the conventional or granular raw material feedstock, but recent work suggests that this difficulty can be overcome.

1.4.2 Processing and the Development of Materials

Processing methods and materials are inextricably linked together: worth-while commercial developments can stem from either source or both. The processor calls for new thermoplastics materials to improve the efficiency and viability of an existing design of machinery, and raw materials manufacturers may encourage the design of new equipment or adaptation of old to make the best use of existing materials.

The processability of a given material is extremely important. For example, the polyimides and PTFE can only be processed by special high-temperature techniques which do not fall within the realms of conventional thermoplastics technology. Thus, attractive though the properties of these materials are, their high cost and the difficulties associated with converting raw material into finished products have severely hampered substantial growth of sales, although in applications where their properties are essential, these materials are extremely successful. To improve processability, compromises have been made. For example, PCTFE is a material which can be injection and blow moulded in the normal way (unlike PTFE on its own), but it lacks the outstanding chemical resistance of PTFE. Similarly, nylon and polyacetal compounds filled with PTFE can be readily injection moulded to give stiff and strong components with coefficients of friction which are substantially lower than those of their unfilled counterparts, but which are rather higher than those of the PTFE on its own.

Another area in which strong interactions occur is between processability, strength and stiffness. It is frequently possible to achieve satisfaction in any two of these factors at the expense of the third. For example, an index of the ease of processability is often taken to be a low value of viscosity of the molten material under processing conditions. A decrease in viscosity can usually be readily achieved by adjusting the conditions of manufacture of the material, and this, while not affecting the stiffness, can very easily result in a decrease in impact strength.

There are other ways of achieving a desired compromise. For example, in the development of suitable materials for making beer bottle crates it was realized that a tough load-bearing material was required. Low-density polyethylene, a tough material with rather poor load-bearing properties, was available, as was polypropylene, much less robust but much better able to withstand loads. Judicious synthesis, combining the basic feedstocks from which polyethylene and polypropylene are made, led to the introduction of a 'high-impact' polypropylene which admirably meets the requirements.

1.4.3 Likely Developments

Undoubtedly, work will continue in the extension of current limits on production rate, shot weight and volumetric capacity of existing types of machinery, especially for extrusion, extrusion blow moulding and injection moulding.

There are many consequences to the aim of producing large mouldings at high conversion rates. From a mechanical point of view, high conversion rates involve the use of automatic techniques of handling raw materials; operators cannot reach between the platens of machines to remove the moulding from the mould, thus dictating the automatic removal of the product from the mould; and large, expensive tools will be heavy, perhaps weighing up to 50 tonnes, thereby requiring large cranes in the production shop for handling and setting of tools. It is not difficult therefore to envisage installed costs of at least £¼m, although the large moulding machines may only cost perhaps £150,000. Similar arguments apply to large extruders. On this basis, the larger the machines, the more careful will have to be the risk analysis for investment, and market research will more clearly have to demonstrate that the projected sales can support the level of investment. Indeed, where size limitations impose these restraints on the viability of moulding operations it may be more appropriate to select a different processing method, e.g. thermoforming.

At the other end of the scale, the production rate for small items will doubtless increase. A typical objective is to shorten the dry-cycle time of injection moulding machines, i.e. the time required to push forward and withdraw the injection plunger, and to open and close the mould (but not the time needed to fill the cavity with molten material, to wait for it to cool and then to remove the article from the mould). Another objective, mentioned earlier, is to reduce the amount of time needed to cool the thermoplastics melt to a temperature at which the article can be removed from the mould.

1.5 RATIONAL DESIGN

Previous sections of this chapter have presented a broad picture of technological aspects of the thermoplastics industry. It is now appropriate to enquire what might be the best ways of exploiting what is known about this class of materials.

Experience of dealing with a wide range of problems associated with load-bearing applications of thermoplastics strongly suggests that a detailed knowledge of the chemistry of plastics is very rarely required by the designer. It could be argued that a little basic knowledge of chemistry may assist the designer to understand the chemical terms used in the industry and to explain some of the basic differences in behaviour between different materials, but it will not help in assessing the technical and commercial viability of proposed plastic articles. Far more useful in resolving design problems are data which have a sound theoretical basis, but which define the behaviour of plastics under conditions close to those which obtain in service. Of equal importance is a sound understanding of the significance of these data and of ways of using them.

It will become apparent that the mechanical behaviour of thermoplastics at room temperature is superficially similar to that of metals at high temperatures near the limit of their performance. The informed designer of plastic articles recognizes the importance of such factors as temperature and time under load on the properties of plastics, and designs accordingly. He adapts and extends in a relatively straightforward way the standard techniques of engineering design, e.g. heat transfer, fluid mechanics and strength of materials, to accommodate the properties of these materials, and he grafts the use of these techniques, where they are necessary, on to his general experience of the behaviour of plastics in service and of suitable ways of making articles.

Since the mid-1960s an enormous amount of design data has been published, together with ways of predicting end-product performance, and subsequent chapters of this book discuss the background to and the usefulness of much of these design data.

1.6 FURTHER READING

J. A. Brydson, *Plastics Materials*, Iliffe, 1969.
L. W. Chubb, *Plastics Rubbers & Fibres: Materials for Man's Use*, Pan Books, 1967.
E. C. Couzens and V. E. Yarsley, *Plastics in the Modern World*, Penguin, 1968.
M. Kaufman, *Giant Molecules*, Aldus Books, 1968.
M. Kaufman, *The First Century of Plastics*, Iliffe, 1963.
R. Lushington, *Plastics and You*, Pan Books, 1967.

2

Introduction to Plastics Structure and Properties

by A. W. Birley

2.1 INTRODUCTION

The plastics scene has been set in the previous chapter and, before embarking on a detailed consideration of properties relevant to applicational technology, it is appropriate to consider briefly some of the structural features of this class of materials in order to provide a rational basis for the discussion of properties.

2.1.1 Macromolecules

Substances such as gases, water, mineral acids and many organic compounds (materials containing the element carbon) consist of small molecules. That is, at the ultimate state of recognition of the substance as an individual species, the unit consists of only a small number of atoms. However, during the past 100 years, and particularly during the last 50 years, a number of important materials have been recognized as being based on 'macromolecules', giant molecules which contain many thousands or tens of thousands of atoms. Some of these materials occur in nature (rubber, hair, silk, etc.), whilst others are synthetic (nylon, polyethylene, etc.). They have in common that they are macromolecules.

Macromolecules of technological interest are of molecular weight rarely less than 10,000: compared with water whose molecular weight is 18, the molecules are many hundreds and frequently thousands of times as large. The basis for macromolecules is the ability of some atoms to link to similar or other atoms to form large stable aggregates. Carbon provides the best example of such stable linking and assemblies of the type shown in Figure 2.1 provide examples, presented in one plane, of linear (a) and network (b) structures based on carbon (R is assumed not to participate in chain formation). The real structures of macromolecules are non-planar as portrayed in Figure 2.2 for polytetrafluoroethylene (PTFE).

Macromolecules can be regarded as groups of atoms which are repeated almost indefinitely along the chain, or for network structures, in any spatial

15

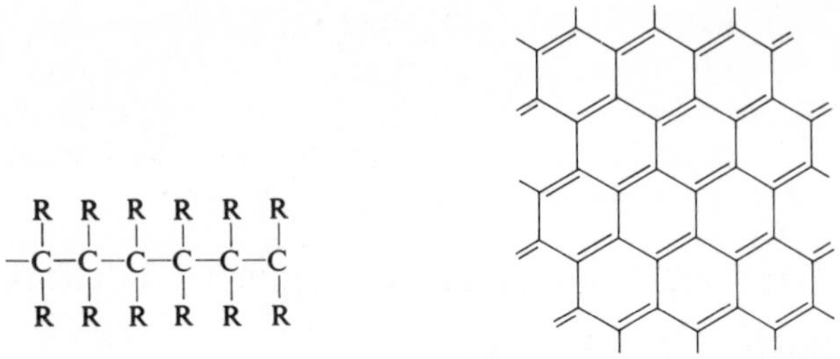

$$-\overset{\displaystyle R}{\underset{\displaystyle R}{C}} - \overset{\displaystyle R}{\underset{\displaystyle R}{C}} - \overset{\displaystyle R}{\underset{\displaystyle R}{C}} - \overset{\displaystyle R}{\underset{\displaystyle R}{C}} - \overset{\displaystyle R}{\underset{\displaystyle R}{C}} - \overset{\displaystyle R}{\underset{\displaystyle R}{C}}$$

(a)   (b)

Figure 2.1 Linear and network polymer structures

direction. Indeed, synthetic macromolecules are frequently prepared by the successive addition of one unit, or 'mer', to another and the product is commonly called a 'polymer' and the process by which it is formed 'polymerization'. The building material is known as a monomer; if only one species of monomer is used, the product is a homopolymer, if two, a copolymer is produced, and if three a terpolymer.

The molecular weight of a polymer is the sum of all the units constituting the chain. There may well be 1000–10,000, even 100,000 such repeat units necessary to develop desirable polymer properties such as strength and toughness, so that it is not surprising that it is extremely difficult to ensure that each molecular chain is exactly as long as every other chain. Since there are many millions of such chains in a gram of product, it is usual to express information about the molecular weight of a polymer statistically, for example

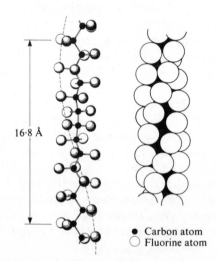

16·8 Å

● Carbon atom
○ Fluorine atom

Figure 2.2 Three-dimensional structure
of polytetrafluoroethylene

in terms of the molecular weight distribution. (Figure 2.3 illustrates two of the possibilities: Polymer A has a lower average molecular weight than Polymer B and B has a broader molecular weight distribution.) Both average molecular weight and molecular weight distribution are important technologically, particularly affecting processing behaviour and toughness, and they are strictly controlled during manufacture. For many polymers several different

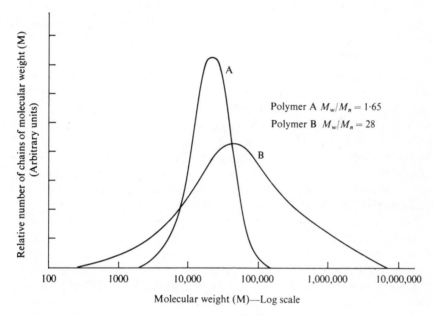

Figure 2.3 Molecular weight distribution for two polymers

'grades', differing in molecular weight, are offered. There are alternative ways of defining average molecular weight depending on whether the contributions of the species of different chain lengths are summed with respect to their number as a fraction of the total number of molecules in the sample (M_n) or with respect to their weight as a fraction of the total weight of the sample (M_w). The ratio M_w/M_n, which must be at least 1, is one measure of the molecular weight distribution. Gel permeation chromatography is a convenient method for determining molecular weight distribution.

The measurement of chain lengths of polymers presents considerable practical difficulties. The principal methods employ polymer solutions in which, at considerable dilution, the interaction between individual molecules is greatly reduced. The averaged properties of the individual molecules then contribute to the measured properties of the solution. Alternatively, the properties of a polymer melt can be examined, particularly its viscosity, which is related to polymer chain length. Solution property measurements which can yield information on polymer chain length include:

(i) osmometry, giving M_n and applicable to high molecular weight polymers;

(ii) ebulliometry (elevation of boiling point of solvent by added solute), giving M_n but restricted practically to molecular weights below 100,000, possibly lower;

(iii) light scattering, from which M_w is usually derived;

(iv) solution viscosity, leading to a molecular weight average between M_n and M_w, and

(v) sedimentation rate in an ultracentrifuge, giving M_w.

It can be visualized that an assembly of chain molecules might take up the extreme form of a random entangled mass or a perfectly aligned system. The latter state constitutes crystallinity if the molecules are also in register along their length. It was established early in the study of polymers that some are indeed partially crystalline: they exhibit discrete diffraction patterns if irradiated with X-rays. The continuing difficulty has been to reconcile crystallinity with the equally well-established long-chain nature of polymers, the feature of the latter being its dominating role in providing a molecular basis for the high elongations observed when polymers are strained.

There are two theories of polymer structure to account for crystallinity: the fringed micelle theory and folded chain crystallites. In each the crystallite dimension in the chain direction is small compared to the length of the molecule so that continuity of the structure is provided by molecules which participate in more than one crystallite, thus linking the crystallites together. A detailed consideration of these two theories need not concern us here: both provide a basis for accepting that polymers can exist in an ordered state and both provide some explanation of why crystallinity in polymers is never perfect. Indeed, the crystallinity level is frequently of the order of 50%. Not all polymers are capable of crystallizing: one of the essential features for crystallization is that the polymer structure should have symmetry. This is clearly achieved in polyethylene and in polytetrafluoroethylene (Figure 2.2) but with polymers

generated from vinyl monomers of the type $CH_2{=}CHX$ there are several steric forms possible depending on the placement of successive monomer units. This is in addition to the obvious irregularity of 'head-to-head' or 'tail-to-tail' placement, e.g.

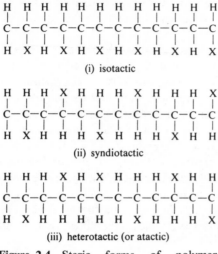

Figure 2.4 Steric forms of polymer [—CH₂—CHX—]ₙ—planar representation

The various steric forms can best be appreciated in the two-dimensional case (Figure 2.4) but shown in three dimensions in Figure 2.5. The three forms are termed isotactic (Figure 2.4i and Figure 2.5a), syndiotactic (Figure 2.4ii and Figure 2.5b) and heterotactic or atactic (Figure 2.4iii and Figure 2.5c). Only the isotactic and syndiotactic forms have sufficient symmetry to be capable of

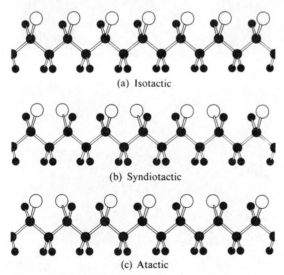

(a) Isotactic

(b) Syndiotactic

(c) Atactic

Figure 2.5 Steric forms of polymer [—CH₂—CHX—]ₙ– three-dimensional structure

crystallization although, if X is very small, crystallization can occur in some cases irrespective of steric factors; otherwise the heterotactic forms of polymers are amorphous.

Although crystallites must be considered as the most important units of structure in a partially crystalline polymer, other aggregates can be of interest and importance in dominating certain properties. Spherulites, radially symmetrical units of structure, were first described a century ago but their importance has only been substantiated in macromolecular systems. In polymer spherulites, the polymer chain direction is perpendicular to the radius of the spherulite. For chain molecules which have different refractive indices along and across the chain, this orientation leads to birefringence, and consequently to light scattering, if the spherulites are comparable in size with the wavelength of light (i.e. > 0.5 μm). Thus, since partially crystalline polymers frequently exist in spherulite form, in thick section they are only translucent. Photographs of typical spherulites are shown in Figure 2.6a and b.

(a)

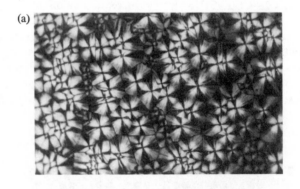

(b)

Figure 2.6 Polyethylene spherulites. (a) Optical micrograph magnification $\times 200$. (b) Electron micrograph magnification $\times 36,000$

2.2 THE PROPERTIES OF POLYMERS

It has been stated above that most polymers are organic in nature although it must be conceded that at least one important class of polymer (the silicones) has an inorganic backbone chain comprising alternating silicon and oxygen atoms (the remaining two valencies of the silicon atoms are satisfied by organic groups, R).

$$
\begin{array}{ccccccc}
 & R & & R & & R & \\
 & | & & | & & | & \\
-Si & - O & - Si & - O & - Si & - O- \\
 & | & & | & & | & \\
 & R & & R & & R &
\end{array}
$$

The organic nature of most polymers, involving covalent bonds and low intermolecular forces, and their long-chain character, lead to properties which are general to the class and provide a background to the more detailed considerations in the later chapters of this book.

2.2.1 Properties Depending on Organic Nature

(1) Low density, leading to light weight and low inertia in moving parts. The relative densities of most polymers are approximately 1 ranging from 0·83 for poly-4-methyl pentene-1 to 2·2 for polytetrafluoroethylene, with the majority lying in the range 0·9 to 1·45.

(2) Corrosion resistance which is complementary to the behaviour of metals. Polymers are generally resistant to aqueous acids, bases and salts but are less resistant to organic solvents. The rough guide that 'like dissolves like' may be found of some usefulness in considering solvent resistance.

(3) Oxidation and particularly ultraviolet-initiated oxidation may have to be considered for various polymers in some applications since oxidative degradation may reduce the molecular weight to a level where toughness and strength are impaired.

(4) Low coefficients of friction are frequently recorded for polymer–polymer and polymer–metal interfaces.

(5) Thermal properties of low conductivity and high expansion are typical of organic materials. Properties can, however, be changed by fillers: in particular, fibrous fillers reduce thermal expansion.

(6) Polymers do not usually have outstanding temperature resistance; they are degraded and/or oxidized at quite moderate temperatures compared with metals and minerals.

(7) Polymers are not inherently opaque: some are transparent, others translucent. Apart from the obvious relevance of this to optical applications (including packaging), polymers can be mass-pigmented or dyed to give self-coloured products.

(8) Since most polymers contain a large proportion of carbon (and frequently hydrogen), it is perhaps not surprising that many polymers burn. However, considerable improvements in their fire resistance can frequently be achieved by appropriate additives.

(9) Electrical properties of extreme insulation resistance and electrostatic build-up are typical of organic materials. Dielectric losses can be extremely low for non-polar polymers in which case permittivity is approximately equal to the square of refractive index. Polar polymers have higher dielectric losses.

2.2.2 Properties Dependent on Macromolecular Structure

(1) Many basic processes which involve co-operative reorganization of the polymer chains are markedly time-dependent. Thus, for a polymer capable of crystallizing, the crystallization process itself is very time-dependent. Typically, polypropylene has a melting point of 170°C but a polypropylene melt cooled from 220°C and held at 135°C requires some $1\frac{1}{2}$ hours for the crystallization process to be substantially complete. The corresponding time for crystallization at 120°C is a few minutes. The interplay between crystallization rate and the time-temperature treatment imposed in a fabrication process has an important effect on the state and properties of the final product. Mechanical properties such as stiffness and strength are markedly time-dependent and are covered in detail in later chapters.

(2) Polymer melts and polymer solutions have high viscosities since relative motion of the molecular chains is impeded by their lengths. In the extreme, entanglement of the chains results in markedly viscous behaviour and this entangled state is relevant for most high polymer melts and solutions. The viscosity is often very dependent on the types of strains imposed and the rate of straining.

(3) High reversible extensibility ('high elasticity') is a property dependent on long-chain nature, whereby the large extensions are accommodated, without failure, by the stretching out or alignment of molecular chains which in the unstressed state are in a random entangled mass.

(4) Stiffness and strength are low for unoriented or unreinforced materials because the strain in the specimen is due largely to relative motion of molecules, rather than actual stretching or bending of valence bonds, i.e. only comparatively weak interchain forces are involved. Orientation (alignment of polymer chains) increases these interchain forces through more efficient organization and the tensile modulus and the tensile strength are increased significantly. Reinforcing fillers increase the tensile modulus, and sometimes the strength, approximately in accordance with a macromechanical mixture rule.

(5) A most important concept is that of the solid amorphous phase, the glass-like state, which can best be treated in terms of an example. The moduli

of poly(methyl methacrylate) change markedly over a narrow temperature range at around 105°C. Below this temperature the material is rigid; above it, rubbery, and it is, therefore, an upper temperature limit of the usefulness of the solid polymer and a lower temperature limit to the processing of a thermoplastic. This temperature is not a melting point because poly(methyl methacrylate) is not crystalline, and it has been given a variety of names such as softening point, glass–rubber transition, glass transition and relaxation transition. In this transition region, the position of which depends on many factors, there occurs a phenomenon which is almost peculiar to high polymers and which is an important factor governing their mechanical properties.

At low temperatures the molecules behave like a large number of rigid units joined together, their overall shape being determined by van der Waals' forces, molecular entanglement and entropy considerations. As the temperature is increased, the thermal energy in the molecules increases and the individual atoms oscillate with increasing amplitude. In the transition region, these vibrations become large enough to overcome the restricting intermolecular forces and the shape of the molecules can then change comparatively easily in response to an applied stress. At temperatures above the transition region, the thermal energy is so large that the forces restricting changes in shape become very small and the modulus falls to a very low level; the material then behaves like a rubber.

It is unusual to find only one transition: most polymers have two or more. For example, polyvinyl chloride begins to soften at a small transition around −40°C but does not reach the main glass–rubber transition until +80°C. Polyethylene has one transition around −110°C and another around 0°C but it does not become truly rubbery until above the crystalline melting point at 110 to 135°C. It is believed that at minor transitions, segments of molecules, and sometimes side-chains, become free to move, but that the whole molecule becomes substantially free only at the main transition. Even then chain entanglements render the material 'rubbery' rather than 'liquid'.

It is evident that the magnitudes of the various transitions, and the temperatures at which they occur, influence considerably the mechanical properties of polymers. Thus at room temperature, the properties can best be understood by considering the transitions, for example:

(1) Rubber is well above its transition. Therefore it is very flexible and has a high elongation to break.

(2) Poly(methyl methacrylate) is well below its transition. Therefore it is relatively stiff and has a low elongation to break; in fact, it is brittle.

(3) Polyvinyl chloride is below its main transition, but above its secondary transition. Therefore it is relatively stiff and has a moderate elongation to break. It is not normally brittle but it may be so under some conditions.

(4) Polyethylene is above its transition but below its crystalline melting point. Therefore it is soft (although not as soft as rubber), has a high elongation to break and is brittle only under extremely severe conditions.

2.3   FROM POLYMER TO PLASTIC

Apart from the introductory paragraphs, reference has been made only to 'polymers' and 'macromolecules' and not to 'plastics'. This distinction has been quite deliberate and seeks to establish definitions for these terms in that the first two are idealized representations of the long-chain or network structures inherent in polymer science whilst the last term is given to such materials applied technologically. Thus, in the practical case the macromolecular substance or polymer will contain adventitious impurity or impurities arising from its production process as well as intentional additives to achieve specific effects either during fabrication or in the end product. This material can be termed a 'plastic'. There is usually the further limitation to this term that it is applied only to rigid materials used in bulk, since polymers are not neatly subdivisible into sections such as rubbers, plastics, fibres, films, coatings, adhesives, etc. For example, nylon is perhaps best known as a textile fibre but it is also used as a plastics moulding material, as a synthetic gut and as a film.

A further appreciation of the differences between 'polymer' and 'plastic' can best be obtained by considering one particular group of plastics, namely that based on polyvinyl chloride, or PVC. Commercial polyvinyl chloride usually contains traces of other materials such as catalyst residues and emulsifying agent which it is uneconomic to remove. The effect of these impurities is generally to impair the properties of the pure polymer, for example, by reducing its heat stability or imparting colour. In contrast to these largely undesirable constituents other materials are deliberately added to polyvinyl chloride to perform one or more specific functions in the 'plastic' or 'compound'. The precise nature of these additives will depend on the processing method used to convert the plastics material into a finished article and the properties required in the finished article. The main classes of such additives used in PVC formulations are discussed below.

2.3.1   Stabilizers

Every PVC compound used technologically contains a heat-stabilizing system, the main function of which is to improve the thermal stability, particularly during processing. Other stabilizing systems confer desirable end-use properties such as improved weathering resistance.

2.3.2 Lubricants

When PVC is softened during processing it becomes sticky. To ease its flow through the fabrication equipment and thus minimize local decomposition and damage to the surface of the article, an external lubricant may be added. 'Internal' lubricants on the other hand act throughout the body of the melt, depressing viscosity and the heat generated by flow.

2.3.3 Plasticizers

A compound of PVC, stabilizer and lubricant is a rigid plastic having a tensile modulus of 2 to 3 GN/m^2. Such compounds are often referred to as rigid PVC compounds, but more correctly they are described as unplasticized compounds (UPVC). The addition of plasticizers (usually liquids of low volatility) results in compositions which, in general, produce articles of greater softness and flexibility, lower strength and electrical insulation, higher elongation and better low-temperature performance and with a lower maximum service temperature. The effect on chemical and weathering resistance, colour, fire resistance and toxicological behaviour will depend very much on the exact nature and amount of all the ingredients present. Because the presence of a plasticizer lowers the temperature at which a PVC composition softens and can be processed, there is less risk with plasticized PVC of degradation during processing.

2.3.4 Fillers

Fillers are often used to reduce the volume cost of a PVC compound. Toughness and low-temperature performance are generally impaired by them, the modulus and hardness are increased and a less glossy finish is usually obtained. Sometimes, however, fillers are used for technical reasons, e.g. to improve insulation resistance. Fibrous fillers are usually incorporated to reduce thermal expansion and improve mechanical behaviour.

2.3.5 Pigments

Pigments are easily incorporated in PVC. The colour possibilities are limited only by the ingredients other than polymers that are present.

From this survey, it follows that statements about the properties of PVC compounds should be accompanied by a full specification of the composition. PVC has been chosen as an extreme example of the practical reasons for distinguishing clearly between a polymer and a plastic, but what has been said applies in part to most other materials classed as plastics. If it appears that the step from polymer to plastic often complicates the position to the extent that even simple statements about the properties of plastics cannot be made, it should be remembered that there is also the considerable gain that the plastics technologist has more variables at his command, and is therefore able to approach more closely to the requirements of the design engineer in any given problem.

2.3.6 Compounding

There are several ways in which additives can be mixed with polymers. Which way is chosen will depend on one or more factors such as, for example, the properties required in the finished article, the equipment available for mixing the raw materials and for processing the final blend, and the relative merits and economics of storing, handling and processing different materials.

In any mixing process the aim is to achieve an intimate physical mixture with uniform distribution and dispersion of all the ingredients, except, of course, when special decorative effects such as non-uniform patterns and colours are intended. If the mixing has been carried out cold, the compound can be fed directly to the processing equipment, e.g. injection moulding machine, but if heat has been applied, the material will usually be in a form which has to be reduced in some way to particles of a shape and size suitable for feeding to the processing unit. A certain amount of mixing and homogenization will take place in the processing machine itself and modified extruders can be used as continuous compounding equipment. The mixing efficiency of conventional extruders and moulding machines will vary from one to another and depend on the material being processed, but, nevertheless, some mixing operations, for example the dispersion of pigments, are nearly always completed in the processing machine. However, there are certain applications, such as, for example, the use of black polyethylene for articles intended for outdoor exposure to sunlight, where hot-compounded material must be used, irrespective of the type of processing equipment available, to obtain the optimum dispersion.

2.4 THE STRUCTURE OF SOME IMPORTANT POLYMERS

2.4.1 Homopolymers

This book is concerned with the engineering properties of thermoplastics, that is of linear polymers, i.e. materials which soften on heating to a state where the shape may be changed by physical forces and solidify on cooling and for which, in principle, the process of softening and solidifying may be repeated indefinitely. The structure of linear high polymers may thus be represented in terms of the basic repeat units inherent in the chains, for it is these which intrinsically, and by interaction with one another in the same or adjacent chains, determine the properties. The repeat units of some important thermoplastics are as follows.

Polymer	Recognized abbreviation	Repeat unit
Polyethylene	PE	$-CH_2-CH_2-$
Polypropylene	PP	$-CH_2-CH(CH_3)-$
Poly 4-methylpentene-1		$-CH_2-CH(CH_2-CH(CH_3)_2)-$
Polytetrafluoroethylene	PTFE	$-CF_2-CF_2-$
Polyvinyl chloride	PVC	$-CH_2-CH(Cl)-$
Polystyrene	PS	

Polystyrene — PS:

Polymethyl methacrylate — PMMA:

Polycarbonate — PC:

Polymer		Recognized abbreviation	Repeat unit
Nylon 6	} Polyamides	PA	$-NH(CH_2)_5.CO-$
Nylon 66		PA	$-NH(CH_2)_6.NH-CO(CH_2)_4.CO-$
Polyacetal (Polyoxymethylene)		POM	$-CH_2-O-$

Polyphenylene oxide — PPO:

Polysulphones:

$-R-SO_2-$ (R is aromatic unit, e.g. diphenyl ether)

The last six materials afford samples where the backbone-chain contains atoms other than carbon, such as nitrogen in nylon 6 and 66 and oxygen in polyoxymethylene, polycarbonate and polyphenylene oxide and sulphur in polysulphone.

From the point of view of *simplicity of appreciation*, it is unfortunate that real examples of these polymers do not consist only of the repeat units listed. This is perhaps not surprising if one views a polymerization as a sequence of chemical reactions which has to be repeated perfectly many thousands of times. Rogue reactions occurring at the level of only a fraction of one per cent lead to modifications in structure which can have important consequences in the properties developed. To exemplify but not to labour this point, one of the six imperfections which can occur in a polyethylene chain is 'branching', where side-chains extend from the main polymer backbone: only the carbon atoms being shown below

$$
\begin{array}{c}
\overset{\textstyle C}{\underset{\textstyle |}{}} \\
-C-C-C-\overset{|}{C}-C-C-\overset{|}{C}-C-C-C-C-\overset{|}{C}-C-C-C-C \\
\overset{|}{\underset{|}{C}}\overset{|}{C} \\
C\overset{|}{C} \\
\overset{|}{C} \\
C
\end{array}
$$

The sample cited in this formula is of short-chain branching but long-chain branching, where the length of the side-chain is comparable with the length of the backbone-chain, is also possible. Because branching is an interruption in the regular sequence, the branch cannot be accommodated in the crystal structure and increased branching leads, therefore, to decreased crystallinity. This reduced crystallinity affects a whole range of properties. This is exemplified by comparing the properties of high-density polyethylene with those of the low-density product (Table 2.1) the latter product being manufactured under high-temperature (and high-pressure) conditions conducive to branching.

Table 2.1 Comparison of High Density and Low Density Polyethylene

	HDPE	LDPE
Branching: chain ends/1000 carbon atoms	2	25
Attainable crystallinity	~85%	~65%
Young's modulus	1380 MN/m^2	170 MN/m^2
Relative density	0·96	0·92
Crystalline melting point	131°C	115°C

Information on chain structure of polymers can be obtained from molecular spectroscopy, particularly infrared and Raman, and nuclear magnetic resonance spectroscopy.

2.4.2 Copolymers

Polymers can be produced by combining two or more monomers to give products with distinctive properties, thus multiplying the number of possible polymers very considerably. For a binary system based on monomers 'A' and 'B' the following possibilities exist and examples can be cited:

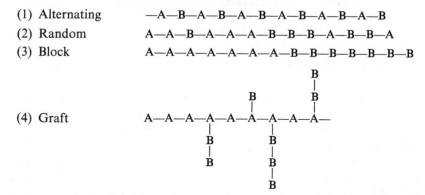

(1) Alternating   —A—B—A—B—A—B—A—B—A—B—A—B

(2) Random   A—A—B—A—A—A—B—B—B—A—B—B—A

(3) Block   A—A—A—A—A—A—A—B—B—B—B—B—B—B

(4) Graft

Many copolymers are used technologically, conferring special properties, e.g. the flow behaviour of PVC is considerably improved by incorporating vinyl acetate as comonomer, enabling long-playing gramophone records of high quality to be produced. Again, the thermal stability of polyoxymethylene is improved by incorporation of units —CH_2—CH_2—O— in the chain, yielding 'acetal copolymer' or 'oxymethylene copolymer'.

If either of the comonomers yields a crystalline homopolymer, then co-polymerization can have a very marked effect on properties by inhibiting crystallization, e.g. polyethylene crystallinity is decreased as increasing quantity of vinyl acetate is copolymerized leading to softer, tougher products.

2.5 FURTHER READING

J. A. Brydson, *Plastics Materials*, 2nd Edition, Iliffe, 1969.

L. Mandelkern, *Crystallization of Polymers*, McGraw-Hill, 1964.

P. Meares, *Polymers—Structures and Bulk Properties*, Van Nostrand, 1965.

F. Rodriguez, *Principles of Polymer Systems*, McGraw-Hill, 1970.

A. Sharples, *Introduction to Polymer Crystallization*, Arnold, 1966.

A. V. Tobolsky and N. F. Mark, *Polymer Science and Materials*, Wiley–Interscience, 1971.

Various, *Characterisation of Macromolecular Structure*, Publication 1573, National Academy of Sciences, Washington, 1968.

3

Deformational Behaviour

by S. Turner

3.1 INTRODUCTION

Within the context of engineering or other structural applications, plastics compare unfavourably with traditional materials such as wood and metals because their moduli are relatively low, even when allowance is made for the advantageous low density of plastics. However, it transpires that these lower moduli are not really a serious disadvantage because a suitable choice of component geometry can often provide a complete compensation. It is not generally very difficult to introduce appropriate changes of geometry and there are new possibilities in recent innovations such as integral-skin, foamed-core mouldings that provide stiffness, particularly in flexure, at low cost and low weight. Glass-fibre reinforcement, in the form of short fibres in thermoplastics and of longer aligned fibres in thermosetting resins, is similarly effective, this time in increasing modulus.

Nevertheless, a real problem does exist. The relatively loose molecular structure of polymers, which is the primary cause of the low moduli, entails a dependence of mechanical properties on the temperature and on the elapsed time under load, and this feature dominates all design procedures for plastics, because the data that are used in calculations must be appropriate to the conditions of service.

Apart from these complexities, there is some difficulty with the background theory. It was widely recognized during the 19th century that the deformational behaviour of many technologically important materials was more complicated than the mathematical formulations of the classical theories would suggest. This is true also of plastics, though a new theory, which fits at least some of the facts, has been developed. In this theory stress and strain are related by equations analogous to those of elasticity theory and, despite the greater complexity of the formal equations, moduli and compliances† can be defined mathematically and measured practically. A sensitivity to elapsed time is classified as viscoelastic behaviour, a terminology which arose from the early

---

† In isotropic elasticity theory compliance is the reciprocal of modulus. It is not necessarily a simple reciprocal in anisotropic elasticity theory or in viscoelasticity theory.

use of spring-dashpot models to represent time-dependent stress-strain characteristics. The fully developed theory, which dispenses with the simple mechanical models, shows that the deformation behaviour of a linear visco-elastic material can be fully characterized either by experiments in which the applied stress (or strain) fluctuates sinusoidally with time or by experiments in which it is established instantaneously and held constant thereafter (step-function experiments). However, most plastics are non-linear viscoelastic under typical service conditions and such materials cannot be fully charac-terized by these experiments.

The current situation is that the linear theory has been extended by essen-tially *ad hoc* methods to embrace the more important practical cases and methods have been devised for the presentation of data in forms suitable for utilization in design calculations. This chapter discusses the more important features of deformation behaviour that are relevant to mechanical engineering design.

3.2 VISCOELASTICITY

3.2.1 Basic Principles

The deformational behaviour of plastics is classed as viscoelastic. The term was originally intended to imply that the properties are essentially a com-bination of viscous and elastic characteristics, but it should not be interpreted in this way in relation to those plastics used as engineering materials because viscous flow seldom contributes to the deformation below the yield point.†　For instance, the strain arising during creep is nearly always fully recoverable. In the absence of an authenticated viscous component, 'viscoelastic' may be taken in this chapter to mean simply 'time-dependent elastic'.

All pre-yield and some post-yield deformation phenomena in plastics fall within the domain of viscoelasticity theory. This is analogous to elasticity theory with the addition of a third variable, time. The simplest case is that of linear viscoelasticity, in which the three variables are related by a linear differential equation.

The behaviour of a linear system may be characterized by its response to any of a number of simple excitation functions, two of which are particularly favoured because of their fundamental significance and their practical con-venience. One defines the so-called complex modulus, or its reciprocal the complex compliance; it is obtained from an experiment in which the excitation is a stress or a strain which varies sinusoidally with time. The other defines

---

† At first sight this might seem to be self-evident, 'yield point' being taken as the point at which irreversible deformations occur. This oversimplifies the associated phenomena.

either the relaxation modulus or the creep compliance, derived from experiments in which the excitation, strain or stress respectively, is applied as a step function of time. The excitations and the response functions are shown schematically in Figure 3.1. The response to the sinusoidal excitation is also a sinusoid but it is never exactly in phase with the excitation and hence the

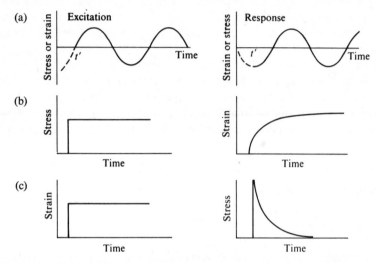

Figure 3.1 Excitations and responses in the fundamental characterization experiments for linear viscoelastic materials. (a) Complex modulus function or complex compliance function (steady state). (b) Creep compliance function. (c) Relaxation modulus function

complex modulus is a complex quantity with a real and an imaginary part. The responses to the step excitations are the sums of many exponential terms.

In principle, any one of the viscoelastic functions suffices to characterize linear behaviour, because there are formal relationships between them. In practice, none can be measured accurately over the whole range of the variables and the choice of technique is governed by a compromise between experimental convenience and ultimate purpose, with the results of several different types of experiment sometimes being combined.

This comprehensive unity breaks down at typical service strains, where the deformation behaviour becomes non-linear viscoelastic. The formal mathematical relationships are then only approximations to the truth, but this is not calamitous because a general correspondence between theory and reality persists and empiricism can be invoked where theory falters. It has been shown that most of the requirements for engineering design data can be satisfied by step-function experiments, which take the form of either creep or stress relaxation.

3.2.2 Creep and Stress Relaxation

Creep and stress relaxation experiments are almost equivalent as methods of studying the time-dependence of deformation behaviour. There is little to choose between the techniques; each has its virtues and its defects, both are suitable for the study of non-linear viscoelasticity. Creep has been, and remains, the more popular but this is more because of the established preference for creep experiments in metals testing than for any overwhelming technical argument. It was convenient, and it has been clearly advantageous, for plastics to be assessed within the framework of techniques and experience already established for metals.

The term 'non-linear' means that the strain at any particular time is a non-linear function of the applied stress. A linear viscoelastic material can be represented by the formal statement

$$\varepsilon = \sigma f(t) \tag{3.1}$$

where ε = strain

σ = stress

$f(t)$ = a function of the elapsed time, t.

Equation (3.1) is the simplest possible creep equation. An analogous and related expression is

$$\sigma = \varepsilon f'(t) \tag{3.1a}$$

which is the simplest relaxation equation.

The simplest non-linear representation is

$$\varepsilon = g(\sigma) . f(t) \tag{3.2}$$

where $g(\sigma)$ is a function of the stress.

A more likely form is

$$\varepsilon = F(\sigma, t) \tag{3.3}$$

Equation (3.1) is clearly a special form of equation (3.2), which is a special form of equation (3.3).

Many specific equations have been proposed to represent the creep of different plastics but none has universal applicability, the best probably being the hyperbolic sine equation of Findley.[1] This has the form

$$\varepsilon = A \sinh B\sigma + Ct^n \sinh D\sigma \tag{3.4}$$

where A, B, C, D and n are material constants. It has a sound physical basis but the values of the coefficients as derived from experimental results are not always in good agreement with what might be expected from alternative arguments and clearly equation (3.4) oversimplifies the phenomena, as do all creep equations. To a lesser degree, stress relaxation equations have also been proposed from time to time.

An evaluation of the creep of an isotropic linear viscoelastic material requires a single creep curve for each of two independent deformation modes (corresponding to the two independent constants required for an isotropic linear elastic material). The evaluation of a non-linear viscoelastic material requires a family of creep curves for each mode, because the response is not proportional to the applied stress (this is demonstrated in Figure 3.2(c) but see section 3.3.1).

At first sight the consequences of non-linearity may seem to be merely an increase in the number of creep experiments but the situation is actually more complicated than that. The main deficiency of a family of creep curves, or the equivalent creep equation, is that it only represents the strain for the simple case of stress applied as a step and held constant thereafter; it cannot be readily applied to a practical design situation in which the applied stress changes with time. Although the creep response of a linear viscoelastic system is similarly defined by a step-excitation experiment, there are not the same limitations on its application because the mathematical theory of linear systems leads to an inherent superposition rule by which the creep equation, $\varepsilon = \sigma f(t)$, can be manipulated to give the response to a varying stress, i.e. to a complex stress history. This rule is known as the Boltzmann Superposition Principle, after its originator, and the mathematical formulation is known as the superposition integral.

There has been a fairly continuous search for a superposition rule for non-linear viscoelastic materials during the past 25 years, with some limited successes, but no one theory has emerged as universally applicable or superior to the alternatives. The current one[2] adds an integral series of higher-order terms to the superposition integral, but it is of little practical use because the number of experiments needed to define the multi-variable functions is very large and the requisite experimental accuracies are beyond the capabilities of most apparatus. The various forms of this multiple integral theory are moderately successful in predicting the response to increasing stress from simple experiments, but they are much less successful in predicting the response to decreasing stress, in particular the recovery following removal of the stress. This is a pity, because recovery is an important practical situation for which data are required and the inadequacy of the theory entails additional testing. It transpires that recovery from a single period of creep and, to a lesser degree, the equally important creep under intermittent stress, cannot conveniently be treated as an inherent part of the creep function or a minor extension to it, as the theory implies; they are separate entities, as fundamental as the creep function, though related to it in specific ways. This independence has prompted an empirical approach similar to that by which the simpler issue of creep was resolved several years ago and this has been similarly successful. This, and another important case of varying stress, is discussed in section 3.3.

The linear viscoelasticity theory was developed mainly in relation to shear, whereas the developments in experimentation and data production have been mainly limited to tension. This divergence arose because simplifying assumptions can be introduced into the theory for shear deformations and yet it can be argued that tension is the most practically advantageous. Other modes have been studied experimentally but not in as much detail as tension. Recently, there have been some studies of creep under combined stresses. The main approach has been based on the equivalence principle, using $\bar{\sigma}$, the equivalent stress, and $\bar{\varepsilon}$, the equivalent strain, defined by the equations

$$\bar{\sigma} = \frac{1}{\sqrt{2}}[(\sigma_1 - \sigma_2)^2 + (\sigma_2 - \sigma_3)^2 + (\sigma_3 - \sigma_1)^2]^{1/2} \qquad (3.5)$$

$$\bar{\varepsilon} = \frac{\sqrt{2}}{3}[(\varepsilon_1 - \varepsilon_2)^2 + (\varepsilon_1 - \varepsilon_3)^2 + (\varepsilon_3 - \varepsilon_1)^2]^{1/2} \qquad (3.6)$$

where σ_1, etc. are the principal stresses and ε_1, etc. are the principal strains.

The principle of equivalence has been shown to be adequate, within the accuracies acceptable for design calculations, for polyethylene,[3] but further work will be necessary to establish the general validity of such an expression because many of the assumptions inherent in the equivalence concept are known to be violated by plastics (e.g. compressive moduli are different from tensile moduli, the shear moduli are sensitive to the hydrostatic compression component, etc.).

3.2.3 Arbitrary Deformation Tests

Simple tests by which limited aspects of the deformation behaviour of plastics can be measured quickly are very popular, and a significant proportion of them have acquired the status of standard test methods. The data obtained by these methods, on properties such as yield stress, tensile strength and flexural modulus, are commonly used to compare materials. They also provide first-order approximations to what is required for design calculations. Used judiciously they are helpful but they have serious limitations that stem from their arbitrary nature. Their apparent simplicity is a deception since they avoid the complexity inherent in polymer properties only by imposing special boundary conditions and special restrictions on the variables. For instance, in tensile testing the crosshead speed is constant and the straining rate may be approximately so; the strength or the yield stress obtained from such a test is an acceptable datum but a modulus derived from the stress–strain curve is less fundamental than those defined by Figure 3.1, to which it is related, but by a complicated integral equation. Not surprisingly, the answers which emerge are correspondingly restricted and subsequent misuse is inevitable. Another deficiency is that each arbitrary test seems to stand in isolation, unrelated to the others, even though they must be measuring different aspects of the same phenomena. However, some unification is possible because many of the standard tests are not grossly dissimilar in nature from those by which design data are obtained; the differences often lie in the imposed conditions rather than in the fundamentals. Advances towards rationalization seem possible through the work of British Standards Institution Committee PLC/36, the first recommendations of which have now been published as BS 4618, *Recommendations for the Presentation of Plastics Design Data*. This committee is not responsible for the revision of existing standard test methods but much of what it recommends constitutes a replacement for some of the older methods and imposes the unity that has hitherto been lacking.

3.3   ENGINEERING DESIGN DATA

3.3.1   Tensile Creep

A tensile creep curve for a nearly rigid plastic is similar in general form to those for metals, though there is seldom a well-defined secondary creep region. Figure 3.2a shows the typical shape when strain is plotted against elapsed time and Figure 3.2b shows the more useful alternative, with log time as the abscissa. There are several good reasons for the superiority of a logarithmic scale for the elapsed time. The main one is the wide range of time over which time-dependence is manifest and important. A second is the facility for extrapolation to longer times, either directly or through some formal stress–time or time–temperature superposition technique (see section 3.3.2). On the other hand, graphical superposition in accordance with the Boltzmann Superposition technique or one of the non-linear variants (section 3.2.2) requires a linear time scale.

The single curve of Figure 3.2b suffices to characterize a linear material because it reduces directly to the linear creep compliance function, designated $f(t)$ in equation (3.1). A family of curves, which do not reduce to a common creep compliance curve, is needed to characterize a non-linear material (see the actual experimental tensile creep curves for a polymethyl methacrylate in Figure 3.2c). An analogous set of curves, showing stress decreasing with increasing time, is obtained from stress relaxation experiments. As has already been discussed in section 3.2.2, these functions are not equations of state; they are valid only for stress or strain applied as a step and can be applied to other situations only if additional rules are known.

Each material has its own characteristic stress/strain/time function, or a family of such functions, and there are two important qualifying comments.

(1) For closely related polymers, e.g. similar copolymers, different grades of one polymer, different processing conditions, the characterizing functions are very closely similar and if one is known others can be closely estimated.[4]

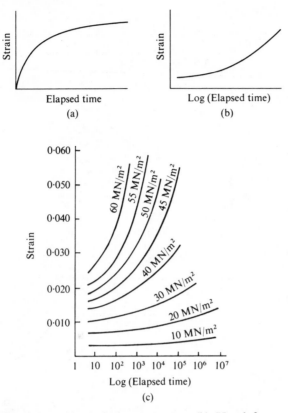

Figure 3.2 (a) Typical creep curve. (b) Usual form of presentation for creep data. (c) Experimental creep curves. A polymethyl methacrylate at 20°C

(2) For unrelated polymers, the corresponding functions intersect and diverge. This complicates all comparisons between polymers, even those as closely competing as polypropylene and high-density polyethylene.

There are several ways in which a stress/strain/time function can be displayed. A family of creep curves is the primary form but cross-sections at constant times (isochronous curves) or at constant strains (isometric curves) are often more suitable for direct applications. The experimental curves are not always as numerous as those in Figure 3.2c and it is then necessary to generate interpolated creep curves by numerical methods if smooth and accurate cross-plots are required. Such an interpolated family of tensile creep curves for a pipe grade PVC compound is shown in Figure 3.3a and the associated isochronous and isometric curves in Figures 3.3b and 3.3c, respectively.

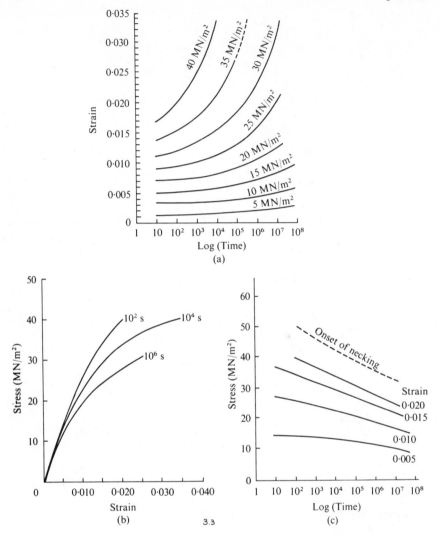

Figure 3.3 (a) Creep (b) isochronous and (c) isometric data derived from experimental results by numerical interpolation. A pipe grade of PVC at 20°C

Any point on any of the curves gives a strain/stress ratio, the reciprocal of which can be manipulated as a modulus (designated 'creep modulus') in design calculations. A distinction should be made between moduli derived in this way, i.e. as the reciprocal of a creep compliance, and moduli derived directly from stress relaxation experiments. The latter is a properly defined physical quantity which is required for design calculations in which the strain is prescribed and the stress is free to vary; the former is not a strictly defined physical quantity (for reasons which emerge from viscoelasticity theory) but is nevertheless the correct property for design calculations where the stress is prescribed but the strain is free to vary. The numerical difference between the relaxation modulus and the 'creep modulus' is often small when the strains and elapsed times are matched and the two can be used interchangeably for most calculations. Creep modulus vs. log (elapsed time) is an alternative to Figure 3.3c.

A basic system of data presented as in Figure 3.3 is specific to one grade of plastic, one material state, one temperature, one system of stress and one particular stressing history. At first sight, this is far too restrictive for general use, and the raw materials supplier may seem to be faced with an unending

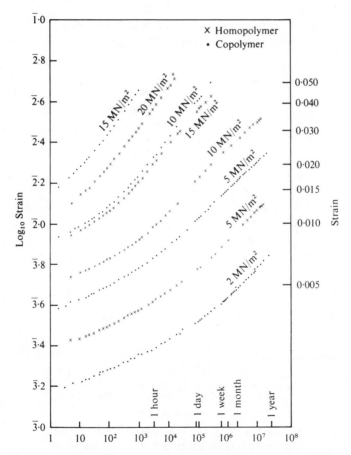

Figure 3.4 Similar creep in different polypropylene grades. Similar shapes allow data for one grade to be used for others

evaluation task as new grades or minor variants are introduced. Fortunately this is not so, as has been briefly indicated above; it has been found that the data for one condition can often be manipulated so as to be applicable for another condition according to rules that are specific to each class of polymer. These rules are based on patterns of behaviour that have emerged from comprehensive studies of creep behaviour. That of polypropylene offers a typical example. Copolymerization with ethylene reduces the resistance to creep but in such a way that the curves for a homopolymer and a 15% ethylene 'block copolymer' of similar melt flow characteristics are very similar in shape when plotted as log strain vs. log time (see Figure 3.4). Thus, if a comprehensive set of data is available for the homopolymer it can be converted into corresponding data for any copolymer provided the shift factors are known; these latter can be derived from a so-called isochronous experiment,[5] which is a special procedure developed to provide one isochronous curve directly, rather than as a cross-section of a family of creep curves.

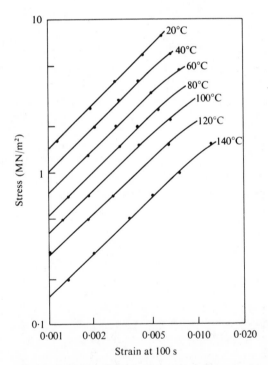

Figure 3.5 The effect of temperature on the 100 second isochronous stress–strain curve of propylene homopolymer, density 912 KG/m³. Modulus–temperature curves at specific strain can be derived from such data

Similar adjustments or interpolations can be made for humidity or temperature though with less confidence. The principle remains the same: a comprehensive stress/strain/time matrix of data for one particular sample condition or environment can be adjusted so as to be relevant to a different sample condition or environment by means of a factor or factors derived from relatively restricted experiments, generally, but not exclusively, short-time small-strain experiments.

At the crudest level of approximation, a modulus vs. temperature curve obtained by one of the standard test methods, e.g. tangent modulus from tensile tests at various temperatures, dynamic shear modulus by torsion pendulum, can be used to provide the adjustment factors. A more reliable estimate would incorporate the effects of higher strain; stress/strain curves from either isochronous or constant straining rate experiments would be suitable for this, e.g. the curves in Figure 3.5. These methods only provide adjustment factors valid at short times, and a prudent investigator would check through experiments covering long elapsed times, i.e. the abbreviated methods for temperature differences are of limited value. Stress relaxation data can be manipulated in the same way.

3.3.2 Properties at Long Times

Normal materials testing programmes readily provide comprehensive information about the stress/strain/time functions for short times, but it is not practical for the experiments to continue over elapsed times of a year or more and therefore the behaviour at such long times has to be estimated. The two main techniques are time–temperature superposition[6] and stress–time superposition;[7] both methods exploit the fact that creep rates (or relaxation rates) increase with increasing temperature and with increasing stress. Their common defect is a lack of quantitative precision, to which there are several contributory factors.

Time–temperature superposition, which exploits a similarity between the effects of a change of temperature and a change of frequency (or of elapsed time), is commonly used for the manipulation of stress relaxation data and is fairly satisfactory for amorphous plastics in the region of the glass–rubber transition, where the modulus can change by a factor of 100 or more in magnitude within a similar time factor. In contrast, it is susceptible to severe experimental errors and is also theoretically unsound for amorphous plastics in the glassy state and for crystalline plastics, i.e. for those materials of greatest interest for engineering applications. Recent modifications to the theory[8] have improved its usefulness in this context but it remains of questionable value.

Stress–time superposition is less well-publicized and has not been as widely used as time–temperature superposition. It is inherently the more suitable for creep data. There are several variants of the procedure, the choice depending on the general form of the creep equation. In all cases, a relatively short duration creep curve obtained at high stress forms the basis of an estimate of the shape of a low-stress creep curve at very long times. However, a very similar effect can be achieved by an intuitive extrapolation of a family of creep curves. Such a process incorporates stress–time superposition by giving weight to the shape of the high-stress curves; it also utilizes the known forms of time-dependence (often an approximation to a power law) and can even benefit from the principle of time–temperature superposition by allowing for any known behaviour at elevated temperatures.

There is no question of predictions up to 50 years being made on the basis of experiments lasting for only 10 minutes; each polymer has to be treated differently but, on balance, it seems that an extrapolation by a factor of three should be reliable, provided the strain is no greater than about 0·02, and even a factor of ten may be permissible in some instances.

3.3.3 Deformation Modes other than Tension

As exemplified in Figure 3.6, the phenomena observed in tension are equally evident in shear, which is not surprising since tension involves a large shear component. However, most of the data published so far have been for tension. The basic reasons for this have been expediency, practical utility and overall simplicity. When other deformation modes are studied it is found that:

(1) plastics are less easily deformed in uniaxial compression than they are in tension;[9, 10]

(2) data on Poisson's Ratio† are complex and a number of important problems warrant further serious study;

(3) the bulk compliance and the creep lateral contraction ratio are far less sensitive to elapsed time than the tensile compliance and the shear compliance, though they nevertheless exhibit significant time-dependence;

(4) the magnitudes of the various viscoelastic functions never relate to one another exactly as one might expect by analogy with the constants for an isotropic elastic solid, for instance the shear yield stress being increased by the application of a hydrostatic pressure.[11]

These findings have emerged from recent research and are being elaborated upon by current studies. In the absence of a comprehensive and reliable theory for behaviour under combined stress one must resort to *ad hoc* methods in design. Thus the greater stiffness in compression can be incorporated into calculations involving simple structures such as a beam and safely ignored in

---

† To avoid ambiguities this term should be replaced by two others: creep lateral contraction ratio and relaxation lateral contraction ratio.

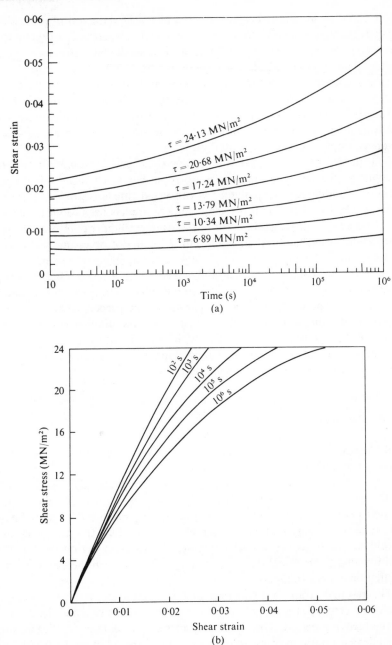

Figure 3.6 Deformation behaviour of PMMA in shear at 20°C. (a) Shear creep. (b) Shear isochronous data

more complex situations because the use of tensile data will provide a conservative design. Poisson's ratio can be assumed independent of time in those situations where its effect on the deformation is small and reasonable approximate values suitable for the calculation of upper and lower bounds for the deformation can be chosen. Bulk compliance or bulk modulus can be assumed independent of elapsed time except where the stress system is predominantly tri-axial. The stresses and strains can be converted into equivalent stress and equivalent strain (equations (3.5) and (3.6), section 3.2.2) which is equivalent to an assumption of incompressibility.

The degree of approximation introduced by such assumptions is often acceptable provided the material is isotropic but mechanical anisotropy is usually introduced when polymer is processed into an article. In extreme cases, generally where the processing temperature has been too low or where the polymer contains high modulus fibres, a larger number of tests is necessary for a complete evaluation than would suffice for an isotropic sample. No major experimental difficulty arises but the cost of comprehensive testing becomes prohibitive and compromise procedures have to be adopted. One such is the derivation of upper and lower bounds to the creep, or at least approximations to them, corresponding to properties parallel to and perpendicular to the main direction of molecular and/or fibre alignment,† and another is the measurement of the variation of properties with angle in short-term tests and an assumption of similar variation at long elapsed times. Each has a particular advantage to offer; neither is wholly satisfactory.

3.3.4 Recovery

If the stress is removed the strain decreases with elapsed time, one obtains what is virtually a creep curve in reverse and, in the absence of a workable theory of non-linear viscoelasticity, such recovery data are almost as essential as the creep data themselves. There are several ways in which they can be plotted and the choice depends on the ultimate use to which they are to be put. The time origin may be taken as the moment at which the preceding creep period started or as the moment at which the recovery period itself started, and the alternative visual displays are very different when the elapsed time is plotted on a logarithmic scale.

The residual strain is a function of three variables, the duration of the preceding creep, T, the magnitude of the creep strain, $\varepsilon_0(T)$, and the duration of the recovery period. Thus, a display of recovery data is one degree more complicated than one of creep data because of the additional variable, and

† This is an oversimplification; the fibres and the molecules are never uniformly and simply aligned.

some manipulation of the data is necessary if they are to be conveniently represented by graphs. This is achieved by means of two quantities:

$$\text{Fractional Recovery (F.R.)} = 1 - \frac{\text{residual strain}}{\text{maximum creep strain}}$$

$$\text{Reduced Time } (t_R) = \frac{\text{recovery time}}{\text{preceding creep time}}$$

which are shown schematically in Figure 3.7. These quantities were introduced initially in an attempt to condense recovery data into a master curve. They are only partially successful in this respect because the individual curves do not

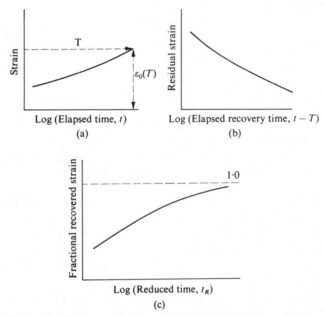

Figure 3.7   Residual strain after creep. (a) Creep (b) recovery
(c) transformed recovery data. Presentation of data is facilitated
by use of fractional recovery and reduced time (section 3.4)

superpose exactly. The trend of the discrepancies is illustrated by some experimental results for a propylene homopolymer (Figure 3.8); several specimens were subjected to different stresses, which were removed when the creep strain reached 0·01. A similar divergence is observed if the maximum creep strains are different and the creep durations identical. The failure to superpose becomes more pronounced as either the final creep strain or the duration of the creep period increases. The use of the derived quantities simplifies the presentation of the data but it does nothing to limit the range

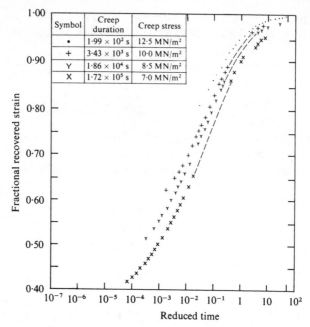

Symbol	Creep duration	Creep stress
•	1.99×10^2 s	12.5 MN/m^2
+	3.43×10^3 s	10.0 MN/m^2
Y	1.86×10^4 s	8.5 MN/m^2
X	1.72×10^5 s	7.0 MN/m^2

Figure 3.8 Recovery after creep, polypropylene at 20°C. Creep terminated at $\varepsilon_0(T) = 0.010$. Recovery delayed progressively as creep duration, T, increases

of the variables. However, although each F.R. vs. $\log t_R$ curve is nominally specific to a particular final creep strain and creep duration it can be used for a range of values of both parameters. Some approximation will be introduced by this, and from time to time it will also be necessary for interpolated F.R. vs. $\log t_R$ curves to be used, but the procedure will be sufficiently accurate for almost all engineering purposes.

The major proportion of published recovery data suggest that residual strains follow a regular, nearly predictable path. If the creep strain has been small (say less than 0·005), the creep duration no more than a few days and the temperature no greater than about 40°C below the conventional softening point, full retraction will occur relatively quickly, though it usually requires a time longer than the duration of the creep period. As the creep strain and the creep duration increase the recovery becomes more tardy, even on the reduced time scale, but in accordance with reasonable, commonsense expectation. The pattern breaks down if structural changes occur in the sample. There is independent evidence to support the contention that this occurs during protracted creep periods and this leads to flatter F.R. vs. $\log t_R$ curves.

In particular, amorphous polymers that creep for a long period (e.g. 1 year) at a temperature very far below their T_g or for a shorter period (e.g. 1 week) at, say, 50°C below their T_g, recover to a far lower degree than is customary for plastics, without necessarily exhibiting any obvious signs of 'plastic' deformation such as deformation bands or crazing.

3.3.5 Creep Under Intermittent Stress

Plastics components are commonly subjected to fluctuating stress in service, particularly short periods of stress followed by long periods unstressed and periodicity corresponding to regular diurnal changes. Recovery occurs during the zero stress periods so that the strain is normally less than it would be under continuous stress and load-bearing sections can be correspondingly smaller.

It has been shown that the strain response to intermittent tensile stress can be predicted fairly accurately by relatively simple calculations based on linear superposition[12] but this was only possible after the phenomena had been recorded in some detail. The idealized experiment is a periodically repeated creep/recovery cycle. Figure 3.9 defines the imposed stress cycle, the strain response and the nomenclature used in the text which follows. In the general case, before the start of the nth creep period there will be a residual strain $\varepsilon_{r(n-1)}$ that is the accumulated residual strain from all the $(n-1)$ earlier cycles. This will tend to decrease during subsequent cycles and, in particular, the strain during the nth creep period will be the sum of this decreasing residual strain plus the new strain due to the applied stress. To a first approximation,

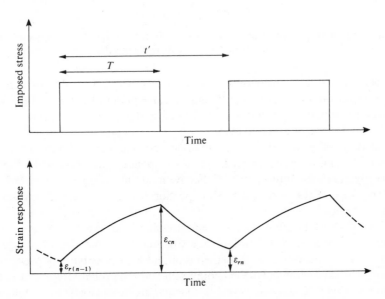

Figure 3.9 Intermittent stress experiment

the additional strain arising from the nth stress cycle should be very similar to that which develops in the first cycle, unless the residual strain $\varepsilon_{r(n-1)}$ is large. The actual behaviour is rather more complicated than this, because of second-order non-linear effects, but the general result is that the maximum creep strain at the end of successive creep periods plotted against accumulated creep duration (i.e. creep period, T, multiplied by number of cycles) falls well below

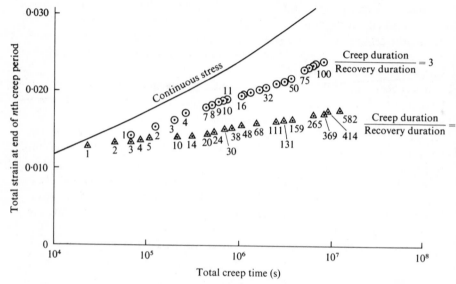

Figure 3.10　Creep under intermittent stress, diurnal cycles. Polypropylene, 20°C 10 MN/m². Numbers indicate cycle number (n)

the creep curve for continuously applied stress. Typical results for a polypropylene are shown in Figure 3.10 and the same pattern has been established for several different polymers (amorphous and crystalline), several stress levels and a range of different cycles.

The data show a surprising regularity and simplicity. Apart from the success of a simple model in predicting the response, the creep data of Figure 3.10 convert directly into a graph of effective modulus vs. log time, Figure 3.11, and the slope of the later straight-line portion can be estimated from simple empirical rules.[13]

There is one limitation. Intermittent stressing is known to promote early failure (known as dynamic fatigue, see Chapter 4) so that the advantage of reduced creep under intermittent stress is offset by the possibility of premature failure. The crystalline polymers endure well and the probability of untoward failure is slight. Glassy amorphous plastics are less satisfactory, but not disastrously so, and the same design method may be applied with impunity

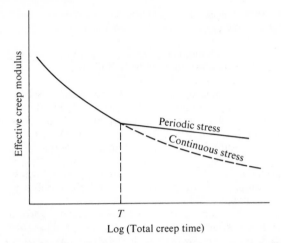

Figure 3.11 Effective creep modulus under periodic–
stress conditions

provided note is taken of the dynamic fatigue resistance; this resistance depends
on the polymer type, the molecular weight and the nature of the creep-recovery
cycle.

3.4 CONCLUDING COMMENTS

The deformation behaviour of plastics is rather complicated, though not
more so than that of metals at high temperatures. It is non-linear viscoelastic
in nature and there is no fully comprehensive theory at present. The lack of
theory is compensated by a sound knowledge of the phenomena on which a
number of empirical design rules have been based. Further advances in both
experimentation and theory are likely but the only area in which there remains
a serious lack of information is that of anisotropic systems.

3.5 REFERENCES

1. W. N. Findley, *Creep Characteristics of Plastics*, ASTM Symposium on Plastics, 1944, p. 18.
2. I. M. Ward and E. T. Onat, 'Non-linear mechanical behaviour of oriented polypropylene', *J. Mech. Phys. Solids*, **11**, 214 (1963).
3. P. Ewing, S. Turner and J. G. Williams, 'Combined tension-torsion studies on polymers: apparatus and preliminary results for polythene', *J. Strain Anal.*, **7**, 9 (1972).
4. S. Turner, 'Data systems for engineering design with polyolefins: manipulations to reduce testing costs', *Plastics & Polymers*, **38**, 282 (1970).

5. D. A. Thomas and S. Turner, 'Experimental technique in uniaxial tensile creep testing', Chapter 2, *Testing of Polymers*, Vol. IV (Ed. W. E. Brown), Interscience, 1969.

6. M. L. Williams, R. F. Landel and J. D. Ferry, 'The temperature dependence of relaxation mechanisms in amorphous polymers and other glass-forming liquids', *J. Amer. Chem. Soc.*, **77**, 3701 (1955).

7. L. C. Cessna, Jr., 'Stress-time superposition of creep data for polypropylene and coupled glass-reinforced polypropylene', *Poly. Eng. Sci.*, **11**, 211 (1971).

8. N. G. McCrum and E. L. Morris, 'On the measurement of the activation energies for creep and stress relaxation', *Proc. Roy. Soc. A*, **281**, 258 (1964).

9. D. A. Thomas, 'Uniaxial compressive creep studies', *Plastics & Polymers*, **37**, 485 (1969).

10. D. G. O'Connor and W. N. Findley, 'Influence of normal stresses on creep in tension and compression of polyethylene and rigid poly(vinyl chloride) copolymer', *J. Eng. Ind.*, **84**, 237 (1962).

11. S. Rabinowitz, I. M. Ward and J. S. C. Parry, 'The effect of hydrostatic pressure on the shear yield behaviour of polymers', *J. Mat. Sci.*, **5**, 29 (1970).

12. S. Turner, 'Creep studies on plastics', *J. App. Poly. Sci. Symposium* **17** (1971).

13. P. C. Powell and S. Turner, 'The transformation of research results into design practice', *Plastics & Polymers*, **39**, 261 (1971).

4

Long-Term Durability

by K. V. Gotham

4.1 INTRODUCTION

In the successful design of load-bearing plastic components, a knowledge of strength is as necessary as an understanding of deformational behaviour. A knowledge of strength involves two major problems: resistance to impact and the ability to withstand sustained loads. The problem of resistance to impact is dealt with in Chapter 5 and this chapter is therefore confined to long-term durability.

A fact which needs to be recognized at the outset of any consideration of long-term durability is that there is no unique criterion of durability for plastics in load-bearing situations. Thus, there may be various stages during the lifetime of a plastic component under load where there are changes, e.g. crazing and stress-whitening, which do not necessarily terminate its usefulness as a load-bearing component but which do, nevertheless, reduce its usefulness for other reasons.

The traditional short-term strength tests for plastics serve a very useful function in quality control but are inadequate as a means of characterizing long-term behaviour. This can be described only by multipoint data covering the effect of elapsed time under load, temperature and other variables. Even with this wider representation, however, such data obtained in laboratory tests may not be sufficiently complete and can suffer from other limitations. For some plastics, it may be necessary to control rigorously the fabrication of the sample, its subsequent treatment prior to test and the test conditions. This can produce a material state which is 'artificial' when compared with that met in service. For example, nylon plastics absorb water to different degrees and the subsequent plasticization affects mechanical behaviour. Since it is difficult to establish reproducible equilibrium water contents naturally and quickly in nylon, laboratory tests are usually done on material in the dry state. In actual applications however, nylon components will rarely be completely dry and, consequently, the influence of absorbed water on long-term durability must be studied separately as a controlled variable.

4.2 LIMITS OF DURABILITY

4.2.1 Fracture

The most obvious limit of durability is macroscopic fracture, which can be divided into two main classes, brittle and ductile. A brittle fracture can be defined as one in which there is no observable plastic deformation in the body of the plastic near or on the fracture surface itself; a ductile fracture is defined as one in which there is irreversible plastic deformation.

As already indicated, macroscopic fracture may not be an appropriate criterion of durability because local stress crazing, cracking or stress whitening may be observed before major fracture occurs and in certain applications such defects may be unacceptable. When this happens these defects become the criterion of durability.

4.2.2 Local Inhomogeneous Deformation

4.2.2.1 *Crazes*

Crazing is most commonly encountered in non-crystalline plastics but similar phenomena have also been observed in certain crystalline ones such as polypropylene and poly(4-methyl pentene-1). The phenomena have been known for many years but development of an understanding of the nature of a craze has taken place largely during the last decade, due mainly to the work of Kambour.[1] A craze is not a true crack, but rather contains polymeric material, interlinking the surfaces of the craze, which has been plastically oriented parallel to the direction of the applied tensile stress responsible for producing the craze. Interspersed amongst the oriented polymer are voids in the form of very small holes which are interconnected to form continuous channels in the craze. The presence of oriented material within the craze confers coherence and load-bearing properties on it. The strength of a craze is important because of its potential influence on long-term durability.

4.2.2.2 *Cracks*

In contrast to crazes, a crack is a flaw in which two new surfaces are created, which are not bridged by polymer, oriented or otherwise. When a crack is being created by the application of a tensile stress there may be a temporary and localized linking of the surfaces near the crack tip. This craze-type material, however, may be weak or unstable and subsequently collapses to allow propagation of the crack.

Qualification of the term cracking by calling it 'stress cracking' is unnecessary since the breakdown of a material locally to form a crack can only take place because a local stress produces an excessive strain, and local rupture occurs. Furthermore, confusion often exists because the term 'stress cracking' is used to describe those situations which more aptly fall into the category of 'environmental stress cracking' (see Chapter 6.2).

4.2.2.3 *Stress Whitening*

This is an omnibus term which covers a range of phenomena in plastics observed as local changes in refractive index of the material. The actual nature of the sources of these changes in refractive index can vary according to the plastic in which stress whitening is observed. It can be caused by microvoids which 'en masse' appear white as the result of light scattering, since they are well below the limit of visual resolution. Alternatively, in heterogeneous materials such as glass-reinforced plastics, it may occur at the onset of breakdown of the bond between the glass fibres and surrounding matrix. Similar phenomena are observed in rubber-reinforced materials, such as the ABS class of plastics, and local breakdown in this case has been attributed by Bucknall[2] to the formation of micro crazes around rubber particles. On other occasions, however, it is equally probable that stress whitening can be observed as the result of microcracking.

4.3 DURABILITY UNDER CONTINUOUS STRESS

For laboratory tests of long-term durability a specimen of the geometry shown in Figure 4.1a has been found satisfactory. With its waisted shape, which produces a linear elastic stress concentration factor of 1·03, the location

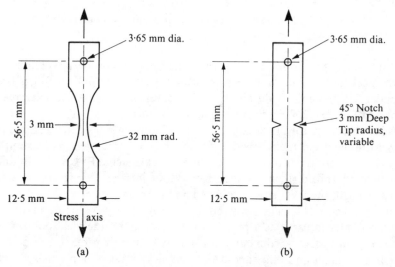

Figure 4.1 Static fatigue specimen (a) unnotched (b) notched

of both local inhomogeneous deformations and subsequent fracture is well defined.

Although ambiguity rarely arises in the establishment of lifetime in laboratory tests when fracture is brittle, when it is ductile there exists a continuum of events covering various states of ductility. Thus, initially the specimen necks

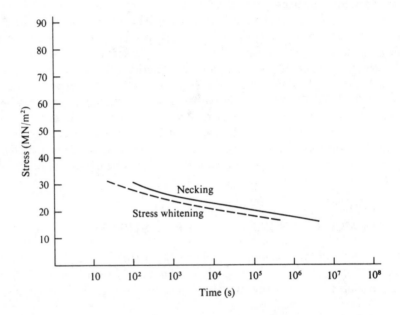

Figure 4.2   The onset of necking in a propylene homopolymer

and this stage may be followed either by necking rupture or by stabilization of the neck and cold drawing[3] but in either case the criterion which has been adopted for the limit of durability is the 'onset of necking'. An example is shown in Figure 4.2, for a propylene homopolymer.

Additional data can be obtained if local inhomogeneous deformations are seen to initiate and their dependence on stress is monitored. For example, Figure 4.3 details the behaviour of a sample of calendered PVC sheet. Initially the material crazed, then, as the creep strain increased under the applied constant load, the PVC stress whitened and eventually necked. The creation of a neck bears sufficient correspondence with the yield point of ductile thermoplastics to use it as a practical manifestation of the yield point. Consequently, in Figure 4.3 the curve for ductile failure by necking can be used as an approximation to the time-dependent yield stress of unplasticized polyvinyl chloride.

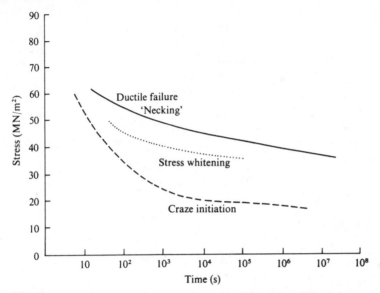

Figure 4.3 Durability of unplasticized polyvinyl chloride at 20°C 65 % r.h.

Further insight into the durability of thermoplastics can be gained from tests on notched specimens, which provide a measure of ductility or brittleness. A suitable specimen geometry is detailed in Figure 4.1b.

4.3.1 Temperature Dependence

As mentioned in Chapter 2, the behaviour of plastics varies appreciably with temperature. It is important, therefore, to establish the effect of temperature on durability. This is most simply achieved by repeating tests done at 20°C at other temperatures, including observations of the initiation of local inhomogeneous deformations as well as other limits of durability.

A typical set of data, in terms of the limit of durability represented by onset of necking, is shown in Figure 4.4 for cast acrylic sheet tested at 20°C, 40°C, 60°C and 80°C. Figure 4.4 constitutes a set of time-dependent yield stress vs. temperature curves from which it may be found convenient to transform the data to other axes by cross-plotting either at constant stress or at constant time.

It is obvious from Figure 4.4 that an increase in temperature results in a decrease in load-bearing ability. For cast acrylic sheet, this is accompanied by a general increase in ductility beyond the yield point, to the extent that whereas at 20°C the material fails by necking rupture, at higher temperatures the neck stabilizes and then cold draws. Since the slope of the curves for durability at 20°C, 40°C, 60°C and 80°C is similar, it is concluded that over this range of

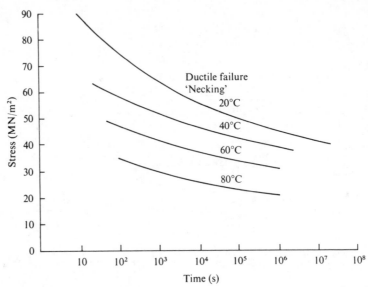

Figure 4.4   Effect of temperature on the durability of polymethyl methacrylate

temperature the time-dependence of the yield stresses is substantially unaltered. Craze initiation follows a similar pattern in that an increase in temperature leads to a decrease in the stress required to initiate a craze. It follows that data of the type shown in Figure 4.4 can be plotted for any other local inhomogeneous deformation that may be observed in a plastic.

4.3.2   Time–Temperature Equivalence

Accumulation of long-term data for design purposes can prove to be experimentally inconvenient and also expensive if it restricts equipment usage. In addition, data are often required for lifetimes well in excess of planned experiments. In practice, requirements for safe working lifetimes of 5 to 50 years are not uncommon. To overcome these deficiencies in the data, recourse is made to the use of prediction techniques.

Several of these are based on the concept of an equivalence between the effects of time and temperature on the mechanical properties of plastics. The validity of this concept is by no means certain but if valid it implies that a knowledge of behaviour at one temperature can be extended to longer times by a study of shorter-term behaviour at a higher temperature. Amongst the more popular methods in use are those employing the principles of time and temperature superposition[4] and theories based on a rate equation such as that proposed by Arrhenius. In these methods data are manipulated either graphically to form 'master curves' or numerically by the use of semi-empirical equations.[5,6]

Tests at higher temperatures are useful since dramatic changes which might occur in mechanical behaviour, e.g. impending brittleness, may be located and serve as a warning of possible behaviour at a lower temperature. At present, however, there is no real substitute for the data obtained at the required temperature because the interactions between material state and temperature are not fully understood. Also, data obtained at a higher temperature and used for prediction at a lower temperature have often been measured on a substantially different state of the material. Overcoming this problem by carefully selected pretesting treatments is not entirely successful, since the resultant state of the treated material is often artificial and unrealistic in terms of service usage.

4.3.3 Deformation and Durability

Since failure could be the terminal point of any creep experiment it is evident that studies of deformation and durability have much in common. There are differences in the respective test philosophies, however, which influence the experimental approach. For creep studies, the main object is to relate the strain response to an applied stress as a function of time, temperature and other variables. Incidental features such as local inhomogeneous deformations, previously detailed, are generally of secondary consideration and microscopic inhomogeneities in strain are ignored. Failure studies, on the other hand, are dominated by any influence which affects mechanical strength and, in particular, by any factor which may cause mechanical behaviour at fracture to change from ductile to brittle. Vincent[7] has described in some detail the material and fabrication variables which are known to influence fracture. Even so, during a study of the durability of a number of different thermoplastics,[8] representing a cross-section of those in current use, a genuine ductile brittle transition was not observed in unnotched specimens loaded at 20°C for up to two years. Failure was in fact predominantly ductile.

Durability data are normally plotted as curves of stress vs. log time to failure. They can be co-ordinated with creep data very conveniently by superimposing isometric stress–time curves constructed from creep data (see Chapter 3) on to the failure curves. This has been done for PMMA in Figure 4.5 and shows that the onset of necking follows a similar time-dependent path to that of the isometric curves, but that the onset of crazing does not occur at a constant strain, at least for times up to 10^6 seconds.

4.3.4 Stress Concentrations

Ductile–brittle transitions can occur, even though they may not be observed when materials are tested under specially controlled and selected conditions and carefully prepared sample states. In fact, experience has shown that

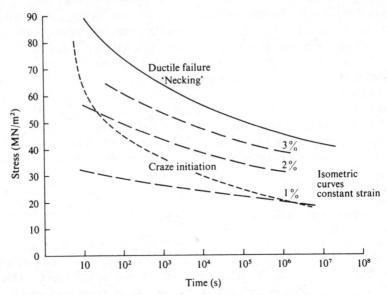

Figure 4.5 Long-term behaviour of polymethyl methacrylate showing combined deformation and durability data

brittle failures occur in service. These can often be accounted for by the presence of flaws or defects seen in the fracture surface. These defects may exist naturally as voids or incipient cracks produced during processing, accidental contamination or even more simply as 'notches' inherent in component design, which act as local stress concentrators which can lead to embrittlement.

In principle, it should be possible to gauge the sensitivity of a plastic to defects from tests made on notched specimens in which severity of the stress raisers can be increased by decreasing notch tip radius, e.g. from 2 mm to 1 mm, 500 μm and 250 μm. The response is often complex and the effect on durability cannot be expressed by a simple stress concentration factor calculated on the basis of the linear elastic theory. More recently, in attempts to design components using a fracture mechanics analysis based on linear elastic theory,[9] very much sharper notches ($r \sim 10\ \mu$m) than those detailed above have been used. However, experience with this type of analysis has not proved it to be universally acceptable, for two reasons. First, although the technique is useful experimentally, in examining phenomenological and micromechanical aspects of a particular problem, as a design procedure it can prove too stringent and unrealistic. Second, there are practical difficulties in preparing truly clean sharp notches in all plastic materials, without causing damage such as crazes or plastically deformed material at or adjacent to the tip of the notch. Additional processes or treatments, either before or after the notching process, which attempt to initiate real cracks from the tip, are generally undesirable since they can expose the plastic to thermal or stress histories which change the material itself.

The severity of naturally existing defects within a component varies and choice of an appropriate safety factor to allow for their influence on durability is difficult. Although it is difficult, therefore, to assess the potential influence of defects on time-dependent mechanical performance and to relate this to design, tests on notched specimens will at least provide a useful guide to a comparison of the behaviour of materials; current experience suggests that a notch of radius 250 μm and depth 3 mm is appropriate for thermoplastics in general.

4.4 DURABILITY UNDER CYCLIC STRESS

4.4.1 Fatigue

In service, the stress will not always be applied and maintained at a constant level; instead it may be intermittent or cyclic and plastics subjected to cyclic loading can, like metals, show the phenomenon of fatigue.

However, the response of plastics to a cyclically applied load is generally more complex than that observed for metals. This stems from their non-linear viscoelastic nature, their low thermal conductivity, and a sensitivity to temperature which markedly affects their mechanical properties. The more important differences of which a designer should be aware are presented in Table 4.1.

It is useful to consider briefly the test philosophy developed for metals. From a design viewpoint, fatigue testing of metals is directed towards obtaining material data in terms of 'fatigue' or 'endurance limit' stresses under a variety of conditions. Component testing is not excluded, being considered necessary in the more involved problems. The data are generally represented by what are termed S/N characteristics, these being plots of the number of cycles (N) required to produce failure at a particular stress (S) on linear-stress/log$N$ axes. In the majority of metals there is a gradual decrease in stress as N increases, producing an 'endurance limit' at a specific number of cycles $N \sim 10^7$–10^8 cycles. For ferrous metals, however, the S/N curve flattens out to reveal a definite 'fatigue limit'. This is a value of the stress amplitude below which a material may endure an infinite number of cycles.

For plastics, the intended meaning of a fatigue test in similar terminology can become obscured, under the same conditions of test as employed for metals, by the factors mentioned in Table 4.1. As a consequence of trying to control or limit the influence of these factors on behaviour, as described by an S/N curve, some modifications have to be made to test techniques in order that the ensuing data are comparative. For instance, the frequency of testing

Table 4.1

Variable	Metals	Plastics
(1) Frequency	Stresses encountered in fatigue testing of metals are generally in the region of or below the elastic limit, so that hysteresis effects are small and frequencies up to even 150 Hz have little influence on fatigue behaviour and can be used with safety. The S/N curve can be developed to values of $N \sim 10^8$ in a convenient test period	Exhibit high mechanical hysteresis. This, coupled with poor thermal conductivity can lead, dependent on the stress or strain applied, to marked rises in temperature. Failure of specimens may then be by 'thermal softening'. To avoid this region of behaviour in materials testing, much lower frequencies (~0·1 to 10 Hz) have to be employed. Test periods may thus become unduly long
(2) Mode of deformation: flexure, uniaxial, torsion	There is little if any difference between results obtained in flexural and uniaxial tests	In view of the different levels of strain energy involved for the different modes, there may be interaction on a frequency basis. (See (1) above.) Because of lack of data, there are no well established correlations between different types of test
(3) Level of the mean load (σ mean)	Except at high temperatures and at stresses in excess of the yield stress at room temperature, the presence of a non-zero mean stress does not give rise to creep during the test	Because of their viscoelastic nature the presence of a non-zero mean stress will give rise to accumulative creep with time as N increases. This will markedly affect fatigue behaviour
(4) Deformation at constant amplitude of stress or constant amplitude of strain	There is very little difference in fatigue behaviour produced by these two conditions of test	Again because of their viscoelastic nature, the response to these two loading conditions is more different than observed in metals. The effect will be more pronounced if frequency is reduced

has to be reduced, the mean load is held at zero, and specimen temperature should be monitored as a matter of course. If, however, for particular applications plastic components are required to operate at high frequencies, then satisfactory working stress levels can only be assessed either by direct component testing or by ensuring that the frequency, mode of deformation, specimen geometry, ambient conditions, etc., used in any laboratory test relate closely to the component and how it is required to function in the application.

4.4.2 The Fatigue Curve

The data obtained with plastics are presented as conventional S/N curves. However, when a square load waveform is used instead of the more traditional sinusoid, the data can be just as simply transposed to a stress–time characteristic. For this purpose time under load in tension is summed over the N cycles to failure to give a time to failure. This stress–time curve can then be compared directly with the corresponding curve obtained from continuously loaded material. Figure 4.6 shows the comparison for calendered unplasticized PVC sheet and clearly the strength of the material is lower under cyclic loading than under constant loading. These experiments were done at a frequency of 0·5 Hz so that there is a 1:1 relation between N (number of cycles) and t (time under load in tension). Figure 4.6 shows also that up to $N(t) \sim 10^3$ cycles (10^3 s) respectively, failure under cyclic loading is dominated by the yield stress. At longer times and lower stresses, the curves diverge, fracture now occurring as the result of crack propagation. By 10^6 cycles (10^6 s) the failure stress under cyclic loading is only 35% of the failure stress under constant loading.

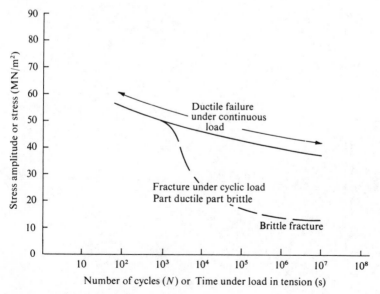

Figure 4.6 Comparison of durability under continuous and cyclically applied loads. Unplasticized PVC at 20°C 65% r.h.

Although for PVC the divergence of the failure stress curves, under cyclic and continuous conditions, is observed at about 10^3 seconds, for acetal copolymer it is not observed until 10^6 seconds and for polypropylene it appears in the region of 10^7 seconds. In general, crystalline polymers are more resistant to fatigue loading than non-crystalline.

Three important points emerge from a comparison of durability under continuous and cyclically applied loads.

(1) The long-term durability of polyvinyl chloride depends on the waveform of the load applied.

(2) Although a ductile–brittle transition in mechanical strength is not observed up to two years with the load continuously applied, it is clearly observable at short times 10^3–10^4 seconds under cyclic loading.

(3) Fracture is brittle under cyclic loading at stresses much lower than the corresponding yield stress.

The effects on the fatigue behaviour of PVC produced by two different waveforms, square and sinusoid, are compared in Figure 4.7. The two curves are similar in shape but, at a given stress, failure occurs at earlier times under square wave loading than under sinusoidal loading.

Brittle fracture is more likely to be caused by application of cyclic loads than constant loads because cyclic loads restrict the growth of plastic deformation at the tip of any incipient 'crack'. For example, in PVC crazes are formed

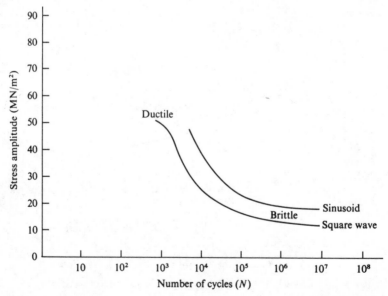

Figure 4.7 Fatigue in unplasticized PVC. Effect of sinusoidal and square waveforms

early in the lifetime when a continuous load is applied. Figure 4.3 suggests that superficially these crazes do not influence fracture, since this continues to be ductile to long times. Because a craze is a local inhomogeneous plastic deformation, it could be argued that under continuous load the plastic deformation associated with the craze continues to increase in size, assuming adequate craze strength. The severity of this defect as a stress concentrator will therefore tend to reduce with time. However, under a cyclic load, growth of the plastic deformation associated with a craze is restricted[10] and the severity of this defect as a stress concentrator is maintained. Subsequent fracture of the specimen is then premature in comparison with the situation for a continuous applied load and the likelihood of this fracture being brittle is increased. The influence of plastic deformation on the nature of failure in PVC is discussed in more detail elsewhere.[11]

Although there is a similarity between the shape of fatigue or S/N curves observed for a number of plastics and those obtained for metals, sufficient experience has yet to be gained to conclude whether a 'fatigue limit' as such exists for plastics. The reason for this stems from a general lack of data and the inevitability of protracted test periods to collect data at the longer lifetimes because of the necessity to use low frequencies. For example, to complete 10^8 cycles at even 5 Hz would require about six months.

4.4.3 Thermal Effects

Because of 'thermal softening' there is often a need to limit the test frequency. A study of the phenomenon has been made by a number of workers with a view to establishing models for estimation of the likelihood of failure by thermal softening. These models are prescribed in terms of stress or strain, frequency, component geometry, waveform, cooling conditions, mechanical losses etc.[12, 13]

It is sufficient in this chapter to illustrate how the S/N curve can be influenced by thermal effects. Figure 4.8 shows three distinguishably different S/N curves measured on 'Perspex' cycled in flexure at 2·5 Hz. The only change made in the test conditions was that of air flow across the surface of the specimen. (T) denotes fracture by thermal softening. The magnitude of these thermal effects is shown in Figure 4.9 which details temperature/stress curves for 'Perspex' cycled in flexure. The stress is raised by increments of 6·9 MN/m² after equal periods of cycling at each stress (10^3 s). Frequency and cooling are clearly very important factors. From an experimental viewpoint, although the increase in temperature caused by cyclic loading can be markedly reduced by efficient cooling of the surface of the specimen, the resultant behaviour of the material is difficult to quantify in design calculations because of unknown temperature gradients. From an experimental viewpoint in comparing

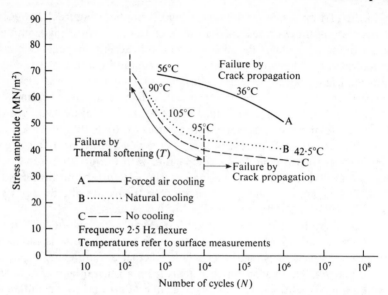

Figure 4.8 Fatigue of polymethyl methacrylate. Effect of cooling at
specimen surface

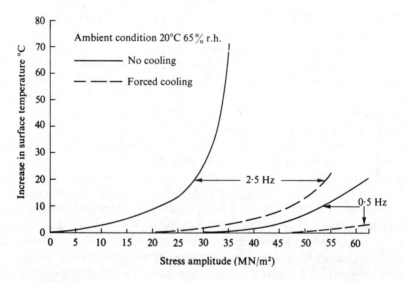

Figure 4.9 Temperature rise in polymethyl methacrylate under fatigue
loading in flexure

materials, it may be better not to 'force-cool'. However, a test procedure has been developed,[14] in which the severity of dissipative heating can be continuously followed and controlled during an accelerated fatigue test.

4.5 DESIGN FOR LONG-TERM DURABILITY

As already indicated, in any situation where a plastic component is required to bear loads, two aspects of long-term mechanical behaviour have to be considered, i.e. deformation and durability. For a particular design either or both these criteria may be important. Deformational behaviour has been discussed in Chapter 3, which indicated that, given relevant data, an appropriate stress or strain limit can be selected for the design of a component. However, dependent on the failure characteristics of the material, this design limit may have to be changed to meet durability requirements. Thus, if after taking into account the variables and factors required by the design specification, the material is known to be still predominantly ductile, then there will be no need to modify the design limits agreed and based on deformation. On the other hand, if any of the factors to be accounted for increase the likelihood of failure becoming brittle it may be necessary to reduce the stress or strain limit below that acceptable for design to deformational requirements only.

For a ductile plastic, direct adjustment of stress or strain limits can be made for variables or factors which are known to influence the magnitude of the yield stresses rather than the nature of the failure. Factors such as time under load, temperature, water absorption and plasticization are likely to fall into this category. Thus, an increase in time under load, temperature, water content, or degree of plasticization may only lower yield stresses and thereby decrease the upper limit of working stresses. The dangerous and troublesome factors to take into account in design are those which change the nature of failure from ductile to brittle. For example, attention has already been drawn in section 4.2 to the embrittling effect of cyclic loading. Consequently, if a plastic component is required to operate under a continuously applied cyclic load, the strain acceptance limit would have to be reduced below that which would have been predicted as acceptable by a continuous load, deformation and failure, criterion. In this case design limits would be dominated by the cyclic loading requirement. Alternatively, the loading history could be between these two extremes, continuous or cyclic. Effects of such intermittent loading on failure have not yet been fully investigated. It is known from deformational behaviour studies that higher working stress levels are permissible because of the benefits of strain recovery, but because the load is cyclic in nature, caution should be exercised in use of these higher stress limits.

If there is any aspect of the load-bearing situation which is suspect or unknown in the sense of its long-term effects on failure, as, for instance, in the case of the component being required to operate in a chemical medium, then either prototype testing or additional laboratory test data are essential to check the acceptability of the design limits selected from pure deformation and failure data.

In designing to avoid fracture of a plastic component which is required to bear load for long times, account must be taken of all relevant factors known to affect the material's long-term strength. Particular regard must be given to those factors whose influence is known to increase the likelihood of brittle failure. Amongst these, the effect of defects or anything which constitutes a stress concentrator remains one of the most difficult factors to account for in design. In assessing a plastic's sensitivity to stress concentrations, so as to apply suitable safety factors in design, it is considered that only by increasing experience with service performance will realistic working levels be found. Current experience does suggest however, that it is quite unrealistic to envisage defects as severe as a really sharp notch, such as is considered in any analysis involving fracture mechanics.[9]

4.6   REFERENCES

1. R. P. Kambour and R. E. Robertson, *Polymer Science*, Chapter 11, Vol. 1 (Ed. A. D. Jenkins), North Holland, 1972.
2. C. B. Bucknall and R. R. Smith, 'Stress-whitening in high impact polystyrenes', *Polymer*, **6**, No. 8 (1965).
3. K. V. Gotham, 'A formalized experimental approach to the fatigue of thermoplastics', *Plastics and Polymers*, **37**, (130), 309 (1969).
4. E. Baer, (Ed.), *Engineering Design for Plastics*, Reinhold, 1964.
5. F. R. Larson and J. Miller, 'A time–temperature relationship for rupture and creep stresses', *Transactions of the ASME*, July 1952, 765–775.
6. S. Goldfein, *Testing of Polymers*, Vol. 4 (Ed. W. E. Brown), Interscience, 1969.
7. P. I. Vincent, 'A working hypothesis of polymer fracture', Institute of Physics and Physical Society Conference Proceedings: *Physical Basis of Yield and Fracture*, Oxford, September, 1966.
8. K. V. Gotham, 'The ductile brittle transition in static fatigue', *Plastics and Polymer*, **40**, 59 (1972).
9. A Van Der Boogaart and C. E. Turner, 'Fracture mechanics: a review of principles with special reference to applications for glassy plastics in sheet form', *Trans. J. Plast. Inst.*, **31**, 109 (1963).
10. P. I. Vincent, 'Localized plastic deformation and fracture', TR No. 97, Division of Polymer Science, Case Western Reserve University, Cleveland, Ohio.
11. K. V. Gotham and S. Turner, 'Procedures for evaluation of the long-term strength of plastics and some results for polyvinyl chloride', *Polymer Engineering Science*, **13**, 113 (1973).
12. I. Constable, J. G. Williams and D. J. Burns, 'Fatigue and cyclic thermal softening of thermoplastics', *J. Mech. Eng. Sci.*, **12**, No. 1, 20–29 (1970).

13. D. A. Opp, D. W. Skinner and R. J. Wiktorek, 'A model for polymer fatigue', Proc. 24th Annual Technical Conference, SPE, 1968, 149.
14. L. C. Cessna, J. A. Levens and J. B. Thomson, 'Flexural fatigue of glass-reinforced thermoplastics', *Polymer Engineering and Science*, **9**, No. 5, (1969), 339–349.

BIBLIOGRAPHY

E. H. Andrews, 'Fatigue in polymers' in Vol. 4, *Testing of Polymers* (Ed. W. E. Brown), Interscience, 1969.
C. Bucknall, K. V. Gotham and P. I. Vincent, 'Fracture II: the empirical approach', Chap. 10 in Vol. I, *Polymer Science* (Ed. A. D. Jenkins), North Holland, 1972.

5

Short-Term Strength And Impact Behaviour

by P. I. Vincent

5.1 TENSILE TESTS

A useful first impression of the strength and ductility of a solid thermoplastic can be obtained from fairly fast tensile tests on suitably shaped specimens. Since the family of materials in question range from hard and brittle to soft and very extensible, a variety of types of behaviour is observed in these tests. It is convenient to classify these types on the basis of the shapes of the recorded load-extension curves. The following examples were obtained by stretching specimens, with the profile shown in Figure 5.1, at a speed of 500 mm/min and a temperature of 20°C.

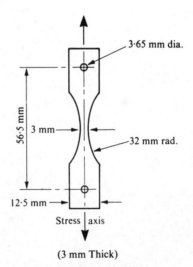

Figure 5.1 Profile of the tensile specimen used to obtain Figures 5.2–5.6

Figure 5.2 shows the load–extension curve obtained with a polycarbonate specimen; this type of behaviour is known as cold-drawing. The stress at the first peak in the curve is the yield stress and is a satisfactory measure of the hardness and the short-term strength in the sense of resistance to plastic deformation. Beyond the yield point a neck forms in the centre of the specimen as the load falls. As the load rises again, the shoulders of the neck travel along the specimen until it breaks.

Figure 5.3 shows the curve obtained with an unplasticized PVC specimen. Again the specimen necks beyond the yield point but there is no cold-drawing; the specimen breaks in the neck before the shoulders begin to travel. This type of failure may be called necking rupture.

Figure 5.4 shows the curve obtained with a polyoxymethylene specimen. This specimen just yielded and then broke with a slight amount of plastic deformation but with no definite neck.

Figure 5.5 shows the curve obtained with a specimen of toughened PVC. Beyond yield this specimen did not form a localized neck; instead the specimen deformed plastically over more of its length.

Figure 5.6 shows the curve obtained with a specimen of PTFE. There are pronounced changes in slope in the yield region but no drop in load beyond yield and therefore no necking or cold-drawing. Thus the yield point is not quite as well defined as in the previous examples. Because of the absence of a neck, this may be called uniform extension. The load-extension relation for polystyrene is not illustrated because it is practically a straight line up to the point of brittle fracture.

A simple and practical classification distinguishes between ductile fracture, in which a yield point is observed before fracture, and brittle fracture, in which no yield point is observed. Thus, all the five types of behaviour illustrated in Figures 5.2 to 5.6 can be lumped together and described as ductile.

The term 'tensile strength' though widely used, needs care because it can refer to three different phenomena which should be distinguished. It is variously used to describe:

(1) The yield stress.
(2) The stress at the break point in ductile fracture.
(3) The maximum stress in brittle fracture—the brittle strength.

Just as the yield stress is a useful measure of resistance to plastic deformation, the brittle strength is a useful measure of resistance to brittle fracture.

Figure 5.7 shows the dependence of yield stress and brittle strength on test temperature for a sample of poly(methyl methacrylate). It should be noted that as the temperature is decreased, the yield stress increases from a low value near the glass transition. At some critical temperature, the brittle point, the yield stress becomes equal to the brittle strength and the type of failure changes from ductile to brittle. With further decrease in temperature, the brittle

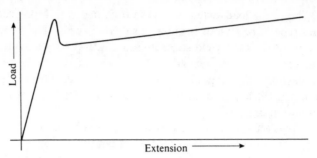

Figure 5.2 Load-extension curve for a specimen of poly-carbonate exemplifying cold drawing

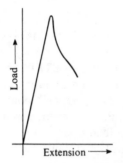

Figure 5.3 Load-extension curve for a specimen of unplasticized PVC exemplifying necking rupture

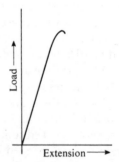

Figure 5.4 Load-extension curve for a specimen of an oxymethylene copolymer. This exemplifies slight yielding without full neck formation

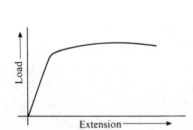

Figure 5.5 Load-extension curve for a specimen of a high-impact PVC. This exemplifies yielding without necking for a composite

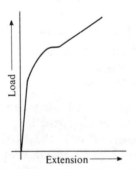

Figure 5.6 Load-extension curve for a specimen of PTFE exemplifying uniform extension

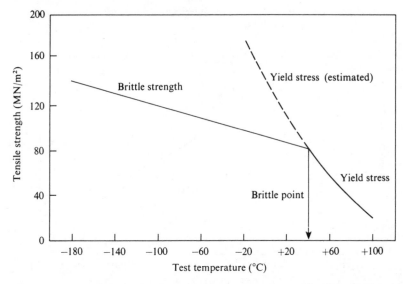

Figure 5.7   The effect of test temperature on the tensile strength of a sample of poly(methyl methacrylate). The yield stress below the brittle point (dashed curve) was estimated from compression tests and from tensile tests on pre-oriented specimens

strength increases less rapidly than the yield stress. (The yield stress cannot be measured in tensile tests in the brittle region but can be estimated from the results of compression tests.)

Various useful data can be obtained from a series of tests of this type.

(1) The magnitude of the yield stress and its dependence on temperature provide an upper limit to a design stress for the material. Figure 5.8 gives this information for several thermoplastics.

(2) The magnitude of the brittle strength indicates the resistance to brittle fracture at a particular temperature.

(3) The temperature of the brittle point gives a first impression of the temperature range over which brittle fractures may be likely in service.

The main practical problem in the field of short-term strength is the question of brittle fracture. The yield stress is a well-defined and easily measured quantity and it is comparatively straightforward to ensure that the yield stress is not exceeded in practice and so to avoid unwanted ductile fracture. It is much less simple to design so as to avoid brittle fracture and it is desirable to understand the ways in which various factors affect brittleness. This centres on a knowledge of the brittle point which, as we have seen, may be taken as

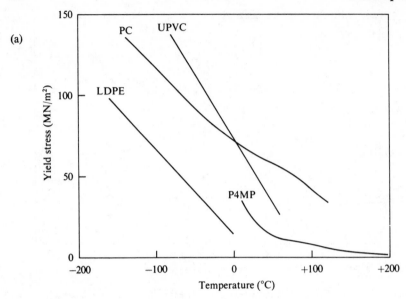

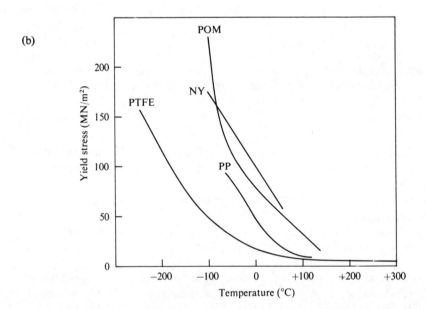

Figure 5.8   The effect of test temperature on the tensile yield stress of eight thermoplastics: (a) LDPE, Low-density polyethylene; P4MP, Poly 4-methyl pentene-1; PC, Polycarbonate of Bisphenol A; UPVC, Unplasticized polyvinyl chloride.   (b) PTFE, Polytetrafluoroethylene; PP, Polypropylene; Ny, Nylon 66; POM, Oxymethylene copolymer

the temperature at which the yield stress is equal to the brittle strength. It follows that:

(1) If the brittle strength is decreased without affecting the yield stress (for example, by reducing the molecular weight) the brittle point will move to higher temperatures and brittle fracture will be more likely in service.

(2) If the yield stress is increased, with a smaller effect on the brittle strength (for example, by increasing the extension speed) the brittle point will again move to higher temperatures.

Many of the factors affecting brittleness are discussed in Chapter 6.

5.2 FLEXURAL TESTS

There are certain practical problems in measuring the tensile strength of thermoplastics in the region of brittle fracture. In particular, if the specimens are machined to the required profile, the result obtained depends on the quality of the machined surface. Thus, without very special care in machining, measured tensile brittle strengths tend to give rather low and unduly scattered results. It is easier to obtain satisfactory results by measuring the brittle

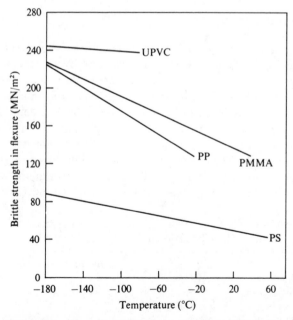

Figure 5.9 The effect of test temperature on the brittle strength in flexure of samples of four thermoplastics. PS, polystyrene. Others as in Figure 5.8

strength in flexure. Usually fracture originates at the moulded surface; fracture origins at machined edges are readily identified and the results can be disregarded.

Figure 5.9 shows the flexural brittle strength of several thermoplastics as a function of temperature. The tests were performed in three-point loading with a span of 38 mm on specimens about 13 mm wide and 3 mm thick; the deformation rate was 456 mm/min. The load-deformation curves were nearly straight and the breaking strains were not more than about 5%. The simple linear elastic formula was used for calculating the brittle strengths. At higher temperatures, where the load-deformation curves are no longer straight and the specimens do not break at such low strains, neither the yield stress nor the breaking stress can conveniently or accurately be determined in flexure.

It is normally found that the flexural brittle strength of thermoplastics is higher than the tensile brittle strength by a factor, known as the rupture factor, of about 1·5. In a detailed study of the rupture factor of poly(methyl methacrylate) it was found that this apparent anomaly could only partly be accounted for by the effect of surface defects and errors in the simple formula. The main reason for the rupture factor is that crazes and cracks grow less readily down the stress gradient in flexural specimens.

5.3 DEFORMATION RATE

As indicated above, when the rate of deformation is increased, the yield stress increases more than the brittle strength and brittle fracture becomes more likely. It follows that tests at a few hundred mm/min are not adequate for determining probable behaviour at the considerably higher speeds of possible service impacts. For this reason it is desirable to extend the flexural tests described in section 5.2 to speeds in the region of a few hundred cm/s. This is most easily done by using Charpy-type pendulum impact tests on unnotched specimens. Table 5.1 gives brittle points observed for several thermoplastics using a test of this type. The span was 38 mm, the width about 85 mm and the thickness about 3 mm; the impact velocity was 244 cm/s.

Table 5.1. The Brittle Point of Unnotched Specimens of Various Thermoplastics in Charpy-Type Impact

Polymer	Brittle point (°C)
Polystyrene	+100
Poly(methyl methacrylate)	+80
Poly 4-methyl pentene-1	+45
Polypropylene	+10
Unplasticized polyvinyl chloride	−50

Results of this type are satisfactory for assessing an aspect of basic material behaviour but are only of limited value for predicting service performance for the more ductile thermoplastics. For example, the tests show that the brittle point of unnotched rigid PVC is around $-50°C$ but brittle service failures are encountered at considerably higher temperatures. For better prediction of service performance from laboratory tests it is necessary to consider the influence of stress concentrations and the use of notched specimens.

5.4 IMPACT TESTS ON NOTCHED SPECIMENS

When planning to use a material it is usually necessary to know whether it is liable to break when subjected to impact in service because it is rarely possible to rule out the chance that it will receive blows or be dropped during its intended lifetime. Ideally, for assessing the financial or technical advantages of using one or another material, one needs to know quantitatively the probability of impact failure in the proposed application. However, this probability cannot be calculated from the material properties measured in the laboratory because the behaviour depends on the details of the material texture and the way in which the article is treated in service, neither of which can be defined sufficiently precisely. This does not mean that impact tests are of no value but it does mean that their scope and significance must be clearly understood.

The particular value of laboratory impact tests is that they provide comparisons of different materials and information about trends in impact behaviour with changes in the base material, fabrication conditions, material texture, design and treatment. But the testing must be sufficiently detailed to ensure that all the important aspects of impact behaviour are examined. For instance, as discussed in section 5.3, tests on unnotched specimens are inadequate for sufficiently comprehensive comparisons.

Brittle fracture in service, at temperatures above the brittle point of unnotched specimens, originates at points of stress concentration such as sharp changes in section or contaminating particles. This type of service behaviour can be imitated in the laboratory by testing notched specimens.

When a notched specimen is subjected to a tensile stress, the material at the notch tip undergoes something similar to a localized tensile test. That is to say, the yield point is reached locally and then the material fails by necking rupture or one of the other types of ductile failure described in section 5.1. The size and shape of the zone of plastic deformation at the notch tip depends on the load-extension curve and ductility of the material. To take two extreme examples:

(1) A sample of low-density polyethylene, which extends uniformly to high strains in a fast tensile test, will have a large plastic zone and therefore have a large energy to break in an impact test on a notched specimen.

(2) A sample of polyoxymethylene, which just yields and then breaks in a fast tensile test, will have a very small plastic zone and a low energy to break in an impact test on a notched specimen. Superficially it appears brittle though, just as with service failures, close examination reveals localized plastic deformation near the fracture origin.

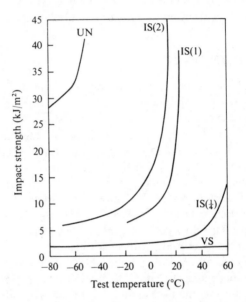

Figure 5.10 The effect on test temperature on five different Charpy-type impact strengths for a sample of unplasticized polyvinyl chloride. UN, Unnotched specimens. IS(2), (IS1), IS($\frac{1}{4}$), Specimens with notch tip radius 2, 1, $\frac{1}{4}$ mm. VS, Specimens with very sharp notches (~10 μm)

It has been found that a great deal of useful information can be obtained using standard pendulum tests of the Charpy or Izod type, provided that the experimenter studies the effect of changes in notch tip radius, test temperature and fabrication conditions. As an example, Figure 5.10 shows some Charpy-type impact strengths of an unplasticized PVC sheet, as functions of temperature, for unnotched specimens and for specimens with four different notch tip radii. On curves of this type, the most important feature is the temperature range over which the energy to break per unit area falls steeply as the type of failure changes from ductile to brittle. This indicates the service conditions within which brittle fracture may be expected. The results on the unnotched specimens show that this PVC sheet was not basically brittle except at temperatures lower than normal usage. The results on the specimens with fairly blunt notches (2 mm and 1 mm tip radius) show that, in the presence of moderate stress concentrations or defects, brittle fracture is possible at room temperature and becomes increasingly likely with only slight reductions in temperature. The results on the specimens with sharper notches ($\frac{1}{4}$ mm and 10 μm) indicate that once established a crack will propagate readily and that, therefore, samples of unplasticized PVC are liable to shatter if they break in service.

5.5 CRACK INITIATION AND PROPAGATION

Figure 5.11 shows the Charpy-type impact strength at +20°C of samples of ABS and polycarbonate as functions of the notch tip radius. The results on the specimens with blunter notches show that the ABS is more liable to be damaged by a blow than the polycarbonate. On the other hand, the results

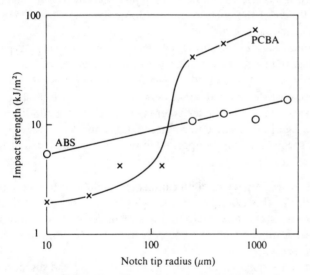

Figure 5.11 The effect of varying notch tip radius on a Charpy-type impact strength at room temperature for samples of ABS and polycarbonate of Bisphenol A

on the specimens with the sharpest notches show that polycarbonate propagates fast cracks more readily than ABS. This illustrates the fact that the concept 'impact strength' covers at least two important mechanical properties.

(1) Crack initiation energy, which can usually be assessed by the results of tests on unnotched or bluntly notched specimens.

(2) Crack propagation energy. Tests on very sharply notched specimens (10 μm tip radius, for example) indicate when this is low.

It can now be seen how comprehensive impact testing of this nature permits understanding and prediction of the comparative performance of different materials in service. On the one hand, a knowledge of the notch severity and the impact energy needed for brittle fracture gives the relative resistance of materials to damage by crack initiation. On the other hand, a knowledge of the behaviour with very sharp notches indicates whether the materials have useful resistance to shattering by crack propagation.

5.6 FABRICATION CONDITIONS

One of the problems of the impact behaviour of thermoplastics is its sensitivity to the fabrication conditions of the test specimens and the final article. Quite a range of conditions may be used for a material in practice and it is not possible for tests on samples prepared in just one way to give the necessary information. Study of the effect of fabrication conditions is an integral part of assessing impact behaviour.

As an example, Figure 5.12 shows the dependence of a Charpy-type impact strength on test temperature for various samples of an ABS. The notch tip radius was constant at $\frac{1}{4}$ mm but the injection moulding cylinder temperature and the direction of the applied stress were varied. The curious shapes of the curves arise because most of the tests were performed under conditions where the crack propagation energy contributes significantly to the energy needed to break the specimen. Some important points can be deduced from these results.

(1) The measured impact strength can depend significantly on the frabrication conditions; in this example, on the cylinder temperature. A compound does not have a single impact strength, even under carefully standardized test conditions. A single value, as frequently quoted in tables, can therefore be seriously misleading.

(2) The impact strength can depend significantly on the direction of the applied tensile stress relative to the direction of flow in the moulding process. Generally, as in this example, the measured impact strength is higher when the tensile stress is along the flow direction than when it is across the flow direction. Since, in service, failure occurs in the weakest direction, tests made with the stress along the flow can be misleadingly optimistic. In particular, a manufacturer who quotes as the Izod impact strength the result obtained on an injection moulded test specimen which was end-gated, gives a false impression of the quality of his material. It is unfortunate that many standard methods for impact strength do not give a more positive lead on this point.

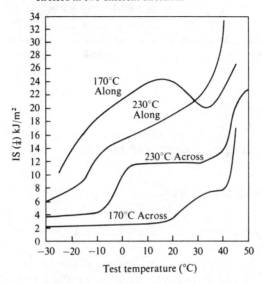

ABS injection moulded at two cylinder temperatures stressed in two different directions

Figure 5.12 The effect of test temperature, injection moulding cylinder temperature and the direction of the applied stress on an impact strength for a sample of ABS

(3) The results obtained with specimens cut along the flow direction indicate that 170°C is the preferred cylinder temperature whereas the tests with specimens cut across the flow show, correctly, that 230°C is better. It is evident that the samples moulded at the lower cylinder temperature were the more anisotropic because of the higher melt viscosity. This demonstrates the importance of the information about the effect of fabrication conditions on impact behaviour and also re-emphasizes the necessity to test across the flow if correct conclusions are to be drawn.

The effect of other fabrication variables, such as the rate of cooling from the melt, will be discussed in Chapter 6.

5.7 OTHER APPROACHES TO IMPACT TESTING

So far this chapter has concentrated on the author's own preferred scheme of assessing impact behaviour. It may be in order now to mention briefly its relation to six other widely used approaches.

5.7.1 Izod and Charpy Tests (ASTM D 256 and ISO R 180 and R 179)

These tests are not sufficiently meaningful because they do not allow for the use of a wide range of different notch tip radii and give no guidance on fabrication conditions or direction of test in injection mouldings. A practical point is that the test equipment is rather inconveniently large for temperature control.

5.7.2 Charpy Test (DIN 53453)

The test is self-admittedly not comprehensive. The square-ended notch prescribed is ill-defined and rather unsatisfactory.

5.7.3 Falling Weight Test (BS 2782: Method 306 B)

This test uses an enormous quantity of material for statistically satisfactory results and is inconvenient for use at other than ambient temperatures. It is unrealistic for the more ductile materials because it produces types of failure never seen in service. Nevertheless the equipment can be useful occasionally, if used in a flexible way, to assess the relative severities of different types of surface finish and also the effect of contamination. It is unsuitable for provision of comparative data on different materials because of its great sensitivity to adventitious defects.

5.7.4 Tensile Impact Tests

Tensile impact tests and high-speed tensile tests are not very accurate methods of studying brittle fracture because the deformation needed to break the specimen is so small. They are more accurate for ductile types of fractures but this is not normally an important service problem. Tensile impact tests can be useful for films, where Charpy tests are inapplicable, but they are rather time-consuming.

5.7.5 Instrumented Charpy Tests

Charpy tests can be instrumented to record the load-deformation curve but the additional useful information is slight and not worth the much greater expense and time involved.

5.7.6 Fracture Mechanics

The methods of fracture mechanics, in which a pre-cracked or very sharply notched specimen is tested and the linear elastic stress distribution is deduced, could be applied to impact. Again, however, the method is expensive and

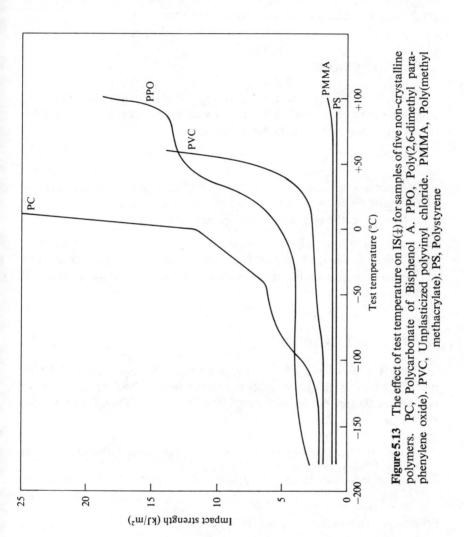

Figure 5.13 The effect of test temperature on IS($\frac{1}{4}$) for samples of five non-crystalline polymers. PC, Polycarbonate of Bisphenol A. PPO, Poly(2,6-dimethyl para-phenylene oxide). PVC, Unplasticized polyvinyl chloride. PMMA, Poly(methyl methacrylate). PS, Polystyrene

time-consuming and, because of the emphasis on very sharp notches, the results do not provide meaningful comparison of materials. Tests on sharply notched polycarbonate, for example, do not expose its good resistance to crack initiation in impact, as demonstrated in Figure 5.11.

5.8 COMPARISONS

Figure 5.13 indicates the type of results obtained when specimens with $\frac{1}{4}$ mm tip radius notches are tested over a wide temperature range. The $\frac{1}{4}$ mm radius notch was selected for three reasons:

(1) It approximates to the most severe defect likely to be encountered in service.

(2) It permits coverage of a wider temperature range than blunter notches, which approximate better to more common service defects.

(3) It matches the widely-used tests mentioned in section 5.7.1.

Five pure amorphous polymers were selected as illustrative because results on composites (such as ABS) and crystalline polymers (such as polyethylene) are so dependent on fine details of the material texture. Some of these effects will be discussed in Chapter 6.

5.9 FURTHER READING

There is a very large body of literature on short-term strength and the impact behaviour of thermoplastics. Many references will be found in two reviews, by the present author, which treat the subjects from the same point of view as this chapter.

'Fracture: short term phenomena,' *Encyclopedia of Polymer Science and Technology*, Volume 7, Wiley, 1967, pp. 292–361.
Impact Tests and Service Performance of Thermoplastics, Plastics Institute Monograph, 1971.

Other papers on impact testing include the following:

BS 4618, Section 1.2, British Standards Institution, 1970.
C. B. Arends, 'Phenomenology of impact resistance and impact testing', *J. Appl. Poly. Sci.* **9**, 3531 (1965).

K. Fletcher, R. N. Haward and J. Mann, 'Rubber-reinforced polystyrene and copolymers', *Chem. and Ind.*, **45**, 1854–63 (1965).
R. A. Horsley and A. C. Morris, 'Testing for performance of thermoplastics, with particular reference to the polyolefins', *Plast. Inst. Trans. and J.*, **34**, 241–50 (1966).

R. A. Horsley and A. C. Morris, 'Impact tests—a guide to thermoplastics perform-ance', *Plastics*, **31**, 1551–3 (1966).

J. R. Thomas and R. S. Hagan, *Meaningful Testing of Plastics Materials for Major Appliances*, SPEJl. **22**, 51–6 (Jan. 1966).

W. E. Wolstenholme, S. E. Pregun and C. F. Stark, 'Factors influencing izod proper-ties of thermoplastics measured with the autographic impact test', *J. Appl. Poly. Sci.*, **8**, 119–40 (1964).

6

Other Factors Affecting Mechanical Properties

by P. I. Vincent

6.1 INTRODUCTION

The previous three chapters have described how the various aspects of the mechanical properties of thermoplastics can be assessed by means of such tests as creep, fatigue and impact and have illustrated how the results obtained depend on the test variables such as time, temperature and specimen notch geometry. The purpose of the present chapter is to show that the results of these tests also depend, sometimes very significantly, on details of the nature and state of the test sample. There are two main reasons why the designer should have some knowledge of the effects of changes in fabrication conditions and in the microstructure on mechanical properties. The first is a rather negative reason: it is necessary, when making use of mechanical test data, to appreciate that they may have been obtained on specimens which differ substantially from the article in service; to avoid being misled, one needs to know the important factors and the kind of difference they can make. More positively, a knowledge of these factors can be of valuable assistance in the choice of compound and in the specification of fabrication conditions for an optimum balance of properties. For these reasons, this chapter is devoted to a general discussion of the effects of various types of additives, defects, crystallinity and thermal history, molecular weight and anisotropy.

6.2 ADDED PARTICLES AND FIBRES

Powders or fibres may be added to the base polymer as cost-reducing fillers, as pigments or as nucleating agents for rapid processing and/or transparency; they may be intended to alter the mechanical properties, to reduce the thermal expansion or to improve the processability and surface finish. Whatever the main reason for incorporating them, they are likely to have some effect on the mechanical properties and it is not safe to assume that the data obtained on samples of the base polymer can be used for design.

When discussing the effect on mechanical properties of adding fillers, or of changing any of the other factors considered in this chapter, it is difficult to be both general and precise. The general picture will be presented, noting some secondary effects, but for a specific design problem there is no substitute for data on the particular compounds in question.

As might be expected, with a high-modulus filler the modulus of a filled material is higher than that of the base polymer, provided that the measurements are made at a sufficiently low strain. The ratio of the modulus of the filled

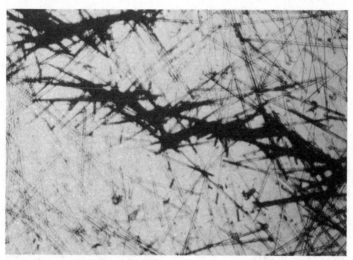

Figure 6.1 A photo-micrograph (×80) of a glass-fibre filled poly-propylene film, subjected to strain, showing the debonding between the glass and the polymer (black lines) and the excess strain in places around the fibres (black patches)

polymer to that of the base polymer at the same strain has been called the enhancement factor.[1] With increasing strain, the enhancement factor falls off with rupture of the bonds between the filler and the matrix and high localized strains in the matrix (Figure 6.1). The practical significance of this effect is clear; modulus measurements at low strains may give an unduly optimistic impression of the reinforcement to be expected from a filler, which may give disappointing results if the material is subjected to higher strains in service. It is essential to study the behaviour in the practical strain range.

The enhancement factor and its change with increasing strain depend on the system under test, including the type and amount of additive, the shape of particles, the aspect ratio (ratio of length to diameter of fibres) and the orientation of the fibres. The strength of the bond between the matrix and the filler is important[1,2] and may be altered by surface treatment of the additive or by

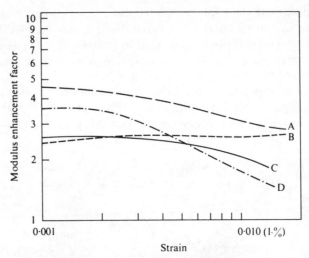

Figure 6.2 Enhancement factor as a function of strain: isochronous tests at +20°C. Propylene homopolymer with various additives[1]. A. 40% w/w asbestos fibre. B. 30% w/w short carbon fibre. C. 19·4% w/w short glass fibres. D. 19·4% w/w well-bonded glass fibres

addition of a coupling agent to the polymer. Figure 6.2 illustrates the effect of a coupling agent in glass-fibre reinforced polypropylene in improving the retention of the enhancement factor to higher strains, and the inferior behaviour with poor bonding in carbon-fibre or asbestos reinforced samples.[1] The strength of the matrix-filler bond is also important in determining failure behaviour. Figure 6.3 shows the dependence of the tensile yield stress of PVC

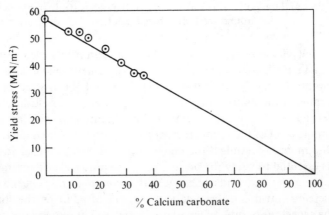

Figure 6.3 Tensile yield stress at room temperature of samples of UPVC containing various concentrations of calcium carbonate powder. Similar results were obtained with other fillers[4]

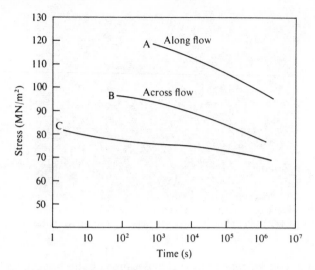

Figure 6.4 The effect of adding 30 % short glass fibres on the failure stress of injection moulded nylon 66 (dry) at +20°C. A. Brittle strength of filled sample. Stress along flow direction. B. Brittle strength of filled sample. Stress across flow direction. C. Necking (yield) stress of unfilled sample

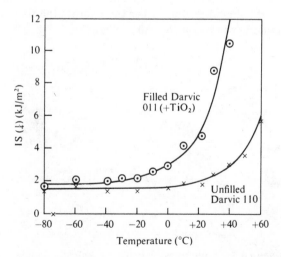

Figure 6.5 Charpy-type impact strength ($\frac{1}{4}$ mm tip radius notches) against temperature for two UPVC sheets with and without 13 % titanium dioxide powder

Figure 6.6 A photo-micrograph (×800) of a sample
of UPVC containing well-dispersed titanium dioxide
powder

on the volume concentration of filler.[3] Because of the weak coupling, the
powders dilute the amount of polymer available to resist plastic deformation;
the yield stress is proportional to the concentration of polymer. In contrast,
Figure 6.4 shows the effect of the good bonding in glass-fibre reinforced
nylon 66.[4] In these static fatigue tests, the unfilled material necked and was
ductile. The filled material was brittle but its brittle strengths were higher than
the yield stress of the pure polymer. Figure 6.4 also illustrates the effect of
fibre orientation; the brittle strengths are about 25% higher when the stress
is applied along the flow direction rather than across the flow direction for
these typical mouldings of nylon 66 + 30% glass fibre.[5-10]

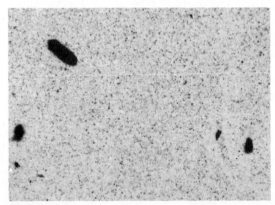

Figure 6.7 A photo-micrograph (× 500) of a sample
of an oxymethylene copolymer containing titanium
dioxide powder. It is mostly well-dispersed but there
are a few coarse particles, up to 40 μm long, which
could act as fracture initiators

There is evidence that fine particles well dispersed can have a beneficial effect on impact behaviour. As an example, Figure 6.5 shows the impact strength–temperature relation for specimens with ¼ mm tip radius notches from two PVC sheets. The filled sheet shows up better than the unfilled. In spite of this apparent advantage of using filled samples, it is often necessary to consider a filler as a possible cause of crack initiation and failure in service. It may be that the particles are not small enough or are not well dispersed. The particle size and the efficiency of compounding can be checked by microscopy on sections. Figure 6.6 shows an example of fine particles, well dispersed. Figure 6.7 shows an example in which there are also a few coarser

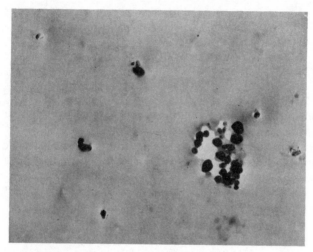

Figure 6.8 An electron micrograph (25,000) of a sample of UPVC exemplifying the aggregation of particles to form a clump which could initiate fracture

particles which are plausible sources of crack initiation. Figure 6.8 is an electron micrograph showing an aggregation of particles. Inadequate dispersion of this type can cause trouble in practice.

Impact behaviour is strongly affected by adding glass fibres. Detailed study demonstrates the effects of aspect ratio, fibre orientation and bond strength but the general behaviour is illustrated in Figure 6.9 which shows impact strength at +20°C as a function of notch tip radius for unfilled and glass-fibre filled nylon 66. The filled material is worse when unnotched or bluntly notched, suggesting that the glass provides defects for initiating damage. On the other hand, the filled material is better than the unfilled with sharp notches, showing that it has more resistance to the propagation of fast cracks. This has the

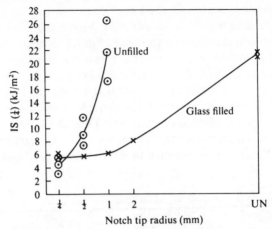

Figure 6.9 Charpy-type impact strength (+20°C) as a function of notch tip radius for dry nylon 66. Unfilled and with added short glass fibres

practical implication that glass-filled polymers are more easily damaged but that they have a greater resistance to shattering.

Figure 6.10 shows a comparison of unfilled and glass-fibre filled nylon 66 in dynamic fatigue demonstrating the substantially reduced fracture strain of the filled material.[11]

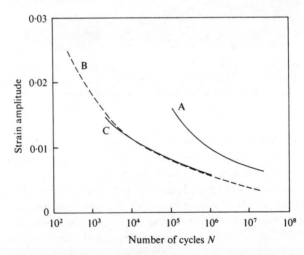

Figure 6.10 Strain amplitude to break as a function of the number of cycles for three samples of dry nylon 66 at +20°C. A. Unfilled. B. Glass-fibre filled. Across flow. C. Glass-fibre filled. Along flow

6.3 SOLUBLE ADDITIVES

Liquids may be deliberately dissolved in plastics in order to obtain specific desirable mechanical properties or for other purposes, namely as stabilizers and lubricants. Alternatively, soluble additives may be unavoidable; water may be absorbed from the atmosphere or the material may have to operate immersed in a liquid which it can absorb. In either event, the normally expected effect is that the liquid reduces the glass transition temperature, thus decreasing the modulus and the yield stress and causing more rapid creep. As the material softens in this way, the impact strength increases; in long-term tests, the failure stress decreases but the softer material is more ductile. These effects are illustrated by experimental results on nylon 66.

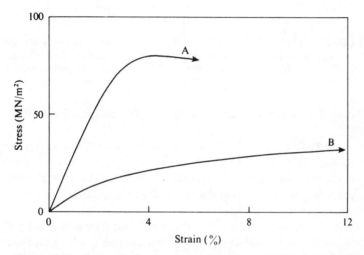

Figure 6.11   Stress-strain curves at +20°C (5mm/min) of nylon 66 dry and after 45 days in water at +20°C. A. Dry. B. With 5·7% added water by weight

Figure 6.11 shows stress-strain curves of wet and dry nylon at +20°C. Figure 6.12 shows the yield stress at +20°C as a function of loading time for dry nylon and after exposure to air at +20°C, 65% r.h. for 11 and 20 weeks.[11] With the increasing exposure to humid air, the yield stress decreases but the ductility increases. Figure 6.13 shows the impact strength ($\frac{1}{4}$ mm radius notches) as a function of temperature for dry nylon and after immersion in water at +20°C for 4 weeks.

Sometimes, the addition of a small amount (say up to 10%) of a liquid has an anomalous effect. For example, the addition of certain liquids to some polymers (e.g. PVC and polycarbonate) reduces the glass transition temperature but, nevertheless, makes the material harder and less ductile at room

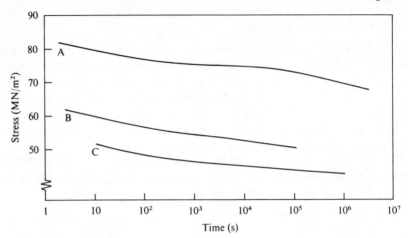

Figure 6.12 Yield stress at $+20°C$ as a function of time under load for nylon 66 (given in part in reference 11). A. Dry. B. After 11 weeks exposure to air at $+20°C$, 65% r.h. Average water content 1.75%. C. After 20 weeks exposure 2·7%

temperature. This effect has been called anti-plasticization by Jackson and Caldwell.[12]

When a thermoplastic article has to operate in a liquid, it may well be that the environment has no effect on the behaviour, particularly of crystalline polymers. On the other hand, several different types of effect are possible and it is necessary to consider whether they are likely to be important in a particular application.

The most obvious possible effect is that the liquid may attack the polymer chemically, reducing its molecular weight and causing cracking and eventual disintegration. For example, strong oxidizing acids attack polyolefines and a range of acids attack polyoxymethylene and nylon in this way.

Some other possible effects may be illustrated[13] by experiments on poly-(methyl methacrylate) at $+20°C$, though this type of behaviour is common to all amorphous polymers and, to a lesser degree, to crystalline polymers. Chloroform is a solvent for PMMA. Benzene is almost a solvent and a strip of PMMA will crack if bent and dipped in benzene. Carbon disulphide is slightly absorbed with some swelling; its presence greatly reduces the critical strain for crazing. Immersion in methanol leads to a reduction in modulus and a substantial reduction in the critical strain for crazing. Cyclohexane is not a swelling agent but it causes some reduction in critical crazing strain.

Some liquids do not attack the polymer chemically and have very little or no effect on the mechanical properties when immersed in the absence of stress. Nevertheless, when the polymer is stressed *and* immersed, there may be a reduction in the critical strain for crazing. For example, this effect has been

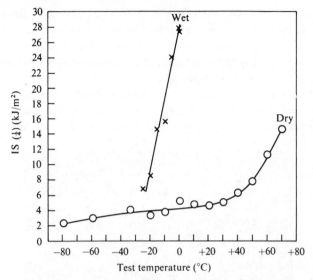

Figure 6.13 Charpy-type impact strength ($\frac{1}{4}$ mm notch tip radius) as a function of test temperature for nylon 66 dry and after immersion in water at +20°C for 4 weeks

observed with high-density polyethylene and polypropylene in the presence of silicone fluids and detergents. With bottles containing liquids under pressure this can lead to excessive leaking and ductile failure. Still more seriously, the combination of an apparently inert environment and an apparently innocuous stress can lead to cracking and a brittle type of fracture. This environmental stress cracking is best known in low-density polyethylene in the presence of such liquids as oils and detergents.[14]

It is not practicable to list all the effects which different liquids have on a range of thermoplastics, particularly when considering the variations caused by changes in molecular weight, molecular orientation, etc. However, it is necessary to appreciate that if an article must operate in a liquid environment, the mechanical properties may be quite dissimilar to those determined in air. Careful and detailed tests may be needed to ensure that the liquid does not contribute to excessive deformation, crazing or fracture.

6.4 BLENDS AND COPOLYMERS

Many thermoplastics are based on polymers made from two or more monomers. The resulting material may be a blend, a copolymer of one of various types (see Chapter 2) or a complex mixed type including, for example, some block copolymer, some random copolymer and some blending. It is difficult to generalize about the effects of blending and copolymerization on mechanical properties because modern blends and copolymers are often complex mixed types in which behaviour can depend quite critically on details of the structure. For any given material of this sort it is necessary to examine the results of a full, detailed evaluation.

Assume that we are starting with a hard, brittle homopolymer of high softening or melting point. This may be intimately mixed on a molecular scale with a softer, tougher polymer. If the two polymers are not chemically

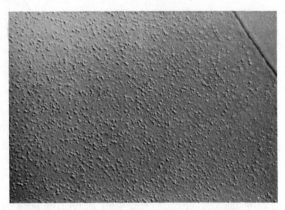

Figure 6.14 An optical micrograph (Nomarski transmission interferometry, magnification 1000) showing a good dispersion of fine particles (~1 μm diameter) of a rubbery polymer in a harder matrix

bonded and not detectable as separate phases, the properties of this molecular blend will be intermediate between those of the two homopolymers.[15] In particular, the softening point of the blend will be lower than that of the harder homopolymer and, for this reason, molecular blends are not often particularly useful. It is more generally valuable to mix the polymers together so that particles of the rubbery polymer, of the order of 1 μm diameter, are embedded in a matrix of the harder polymer. Figure 6.14 shows an optical micrograph obtained from a good blend of this type.

Random copolymers between monomers which would both give amorphous homopolymers usually have intermediate properties. Forming a copolymer from monomers which would give crystallizable homopolymers can give very complex results. Generally the overall crystallinity is lowered with consequent reduction in modulus, creep resistance and yield stress.[16, 17] Figure 3.4 has shown some creep curves at +20°C for a sample of polypropylene and for a sample of material made by simultaneous polymerization of propylene and 15% ethylene. Study of these curves shows that the incorporation of ethylene increases the strain at a given stress but does not change the basic shape of

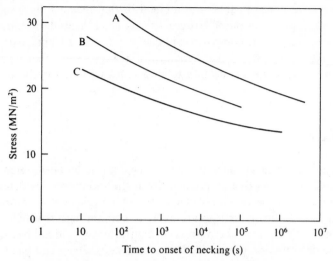

Figure 6.15 Stress to neck (yield stress) at +20°C as a function of time under load for samples of polypropylene. A. A homopolymer. B. With 7% ethylene. C. With 15% ethylene

the curves. Figure 6.15 shows the necking stress as a function of time under load for polypropylene and materials with 7% and 15% of ethylene. Figures 3.4 and 6.15 illustrate the softening effect of incorporating ethylene; Figure 6.16 shows the toughening effect on an impact strength–temperature curve.

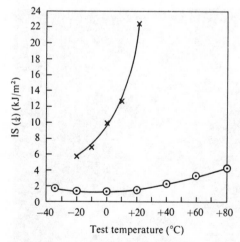

Figure 6.16 Charpy-type impact strength ($\frac{1}{4}$ mm notch tip radius) as a function of test temperature for a propylene homopolymer and a propylene–ethylene copolymer blend

The major advantage of rubber–resin blends is that they can have superior resistance to the propagation of fast cracks[18] as has already been illustrated in the ABS–polycarbonate comparison in Chapter 5. This advantage does not necessarily extend to slow cracks: dynamic fatigue tests show that ABS does not have particularly good resistance to slow cracking under cyclic stressing conditions.[11]

6.5 DEFECTS

Published data on mechanical properties have normally been obtained on specimens which are as free as possible from the more obvious defects. In practice, however, unless care is taken in choice of material, design, fabrication and subsequent treatment, articles are likely to contain defects which lead to local regions of high stress. These stress concentrations would not be expected to affect the deformation properties such as modulus, creep and yield stress, but they have a dominant influence on all types of fracture. Whether in impact, fatigue or environmental stress cracking, the cracks are initiated in regions of stress concentration and, the more severe the defect, the more likely it is to lead to brittle fracture in service. Some of the types of defect which may be found, and which should be minimized or eliminated if possible, are classified under four headings.

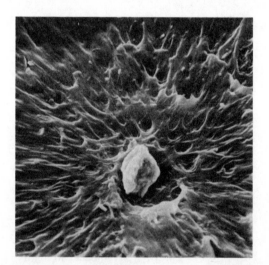

Figure 6.17 A scanning electron micrograph (magnification 2600) showing a foreign body, about 10 μm across, at a fracture origin

6.5.1 Material Defects

Some defects may be inherent in the material as received. It may contain contaminating particles and Figure 6.17 shows a scanning electron micrograph of a particle about 10 μm across at a fracture origin. It may contain agglomerations of an insoluble additive such as that shown in Figure 6.8. Poor dispersion in a rubber–resin blend can leave over-large rubber particles like that shown in Figure 6.18. Too low a molecular weight can lead to small holes and cracks being formed during the cooling from the melt.

Figure 6.18 An optical micrograph (magnification 200) showing a very large rubber particle in a badly-dispersed rubber–resin blend

6.5.2 Design Defects

Some defects may be incorporated in design. Sharp changes in section, holes and notches should be eliminated, unless they are essential for function, and all corners should be rounded as much as possible. Thought should be given to the placing of the gate in an injection moulding; if possible, it should not be in a region of high tensile stress. Trouble may also be experienced if the design involves a layer of brittle material well bonded to the surface of a sheet or moulding; cracks are readily initiated in the brittle surface and then easily propagated through the substrate.

6.5.3   Fabrication Defects

Many service failures have proved to be caused by the use of bad fabrication conditions. Processing PVC compounds at too low a temperature or for too short a time may lead to inadequate gelation and poor bonding between particles. Figure 6.19 is an optical micrograph of a section of a poorly gelled extrudate and Figure 6.20 shows the serious effect that bad gelation can have

Figure 6.19   An optical micrograph (magnification 50)
showing poor gelation in a PVC compound

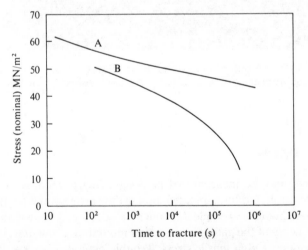

Figure 6.20   Nett failure stress of double edge notched
specimens (notch tip radius ¼ mm) at +20°C as a function of
time under load for two PVC samples. A. Good gelation.
B. Bad gelation (similar to Figure 6.19)

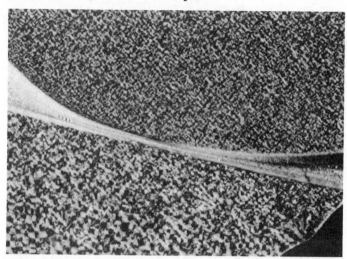

Figure 6.21 An optical micrograph (polarized light, magnification 126) of a polypropylene weld showing the variation in texture which can occur

on the long-term durability of PVC. Similar effects can be observed in in-adequately sintered PTFE. Welding of pipes, etc., is a problem on its own and care and knowledge are required to ensure that the strength in a weld region does not fall too far below that of the base material.[19] A similar problem occurs in injection moulding when two melt streams meet. Figure 6.21 illustrates the texture that can be observed at a weld with a polarizing microscope.

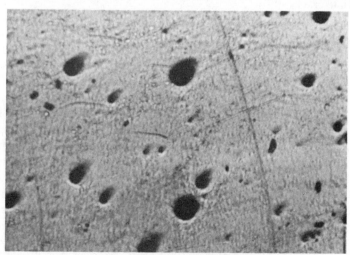

Figure 6.22 An optical micrograph (reflected light, magnification 126) showing pits in the surface of an injection moulded acetal resin

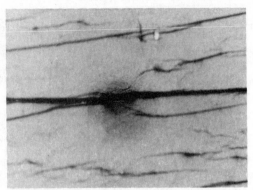

Figure 6.23 An optical micrograph (reflected light, magnification 500) showing a crack initiated, by impact, at a surface pit such as those of Figure 6.22

Bad surface finish, whether caused by incorrect choice of fabrication conditions, rough machining or insufficient tidiness at the gate, can be a potent source of crack initiation. Figure 6.22 shows surface pits in an acetal moulding caused by too low a mould temperature and Figure 6.23 shows a crack initiated at such a pit by an impact.

6.5.4   Defects of Usage

Rough handling in service may cause surface dents and scratches which may initiate cracks.

6.5.5   Designing with Defects in Mind

Because there are so many ways in which defects can arise and because they are so important for crack initiation, it is necessary to bear them in mind during design and to consider how to allow for them. Naturally, the ideal would be to ensure their complete elimination; this course should be followed as far as practicable but cost considerations usually prohibit stringent quality control. The next best approach in design would be to know the type of defect which is likely to exist and to allow for its size and stress concentration factor. Unfortunately this approach is also rarely practicable because of the difficulty of knowing exactly what is happening in a large volume of material. Another possible approach is to consider the worst possible case, a through-thickness sharp crack, as postulated in fracture mechanics; for normal purposes this leads to gross over-design and is only appropriate when cost is unimportant compared with the consequence of even a single failure. Finally, we are reduced to judging approximately the size and stress concentration factors of such defects as are likely to occur and to testing, in the laboratory, specimens containing notches with similar concentration factors. Experience with impact testing has shown that notches about 3 mm deep with $\frac{1}{4}$ mm tip radius represent fairly well the most severe type of defect encountered in service. Much sharper notches (with 10 μm tip radius, for instance) are unrealistically severe and tend to give a poor impression of high-quality materials. At the other extreme, tests on unnotched specimens are often not severe enough to provide a realistic assessment of the liability of a material to brittle fracture in practical applications.

In conclusion, therefore, it seems that a reasonable practical approach to the problem of defects is to take account of behaviour in fracture tests of specimens containing moderately severe notches such as the $\frac{1}{4}$ mm tip radius, 3 mm deep notch described above.

6.6 CRYSTALLINITY AND THERMAL HISTORY

The crystallizability of a polymer is determined by the shape of its molecules, their symmetry, branching and regularity. The actual amount of crystallinity achieved in the solid state is also affected by the thermal history, i.e. the rate of

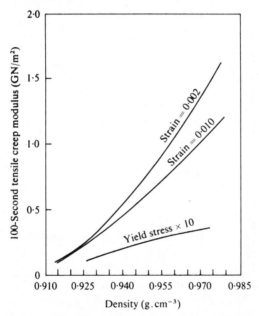

Figure 6.24 The effect of density on room temperature modulus and yield stress of polyethylene[20]. Modulus measured at two different strains; yield stress measured at 50% per minute

cooling from the melt and the times spent within the range of crystallizing temperatures. For detail and precision, it is also necessary to take account of crystal nuclei remaining in the melt and the presence of nucleating additives. Absorption and desorption of solvents can sometimes affect crystallinity.

The problem of relating crystallinity and mechanical properties has not been fully and precisely solved. In essence, the difficulty is that the simple measure of percentage crystallinity is inadequate and it may well be necessary to take account of the size, shape and perfection of both crystals and spherulites and the strengths of ties between units. Variations in the mobility of molecules in the more disordered regions between crystals also play an important part in determining mechanical properties. In these circumstances only general statements about the more clearly proven effects can be made.

Figure 6.24 shows the room temperature modulus and yield stress of polyethylene as functions of the density of the specimens, which is taken as a measure of the overall amount of crystallinity. This illustrates the generalization that thermoplastics become less easily deformable as the amount of crystallinity increases, particularly in the temperature range between the glass transition and the melting point.[20]

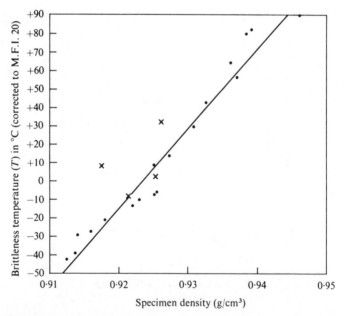

Figure 6.25 The effect of density on the brittle point of polyethylene with melt flow index 20. The definition of brittle point was the temperature at which the Charpy-type impact strength ($\frac{1}{4}$ mm notch tip radius) was 10 kJ/m²

Figure 6.26 An optical micrograph showing cracks between spherulites in an over-crystallized polypropylene

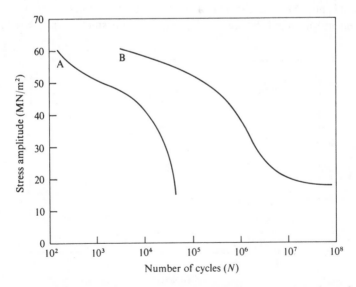

Figure 6.27 Stress to break in dynamic fatigue as a function of number of cycles at +20°C. A. Crystalline acetal resin. B. Amorphous polycarbonate

Increasing crystallinity also tends to move the brittle point in impact to higher temperatures. Figure 6.25 shows the dependence of an arbitrary brittle point of polyethylene on the density of the sample. It was necessary to ensure that the results were not confused by changes in molecular weight and therefore the graph applies to polymers with a melt flow index of 20.

Slow cooling from the melt, or long annealing periods below the melting point, can cause crystallization to develop so far that cracks appear between spherulites, which naturally leads to extreme brittleness. Figure 6.26 shows an optical micrograph of part of an over-crystallized polypropylene.

As a family, crystalline polymers tend to have better resistance to dynamic fatigue at room temperature than amorphous polymers. This is exemplified in Figure 6.27 which shows the inferior behaviour of the amorphous poly-carbonate to the crystalline acetal plastic.

The properties of both amorphous and crystalline polymers can depend also on how long the specimens have been at the test temperature before the test. In general, thermoplastics become less easily deformable and less ductile with increases in the time of storage; quite significant effects can be observed over several weeks with very slight or no change in density. Figure 6.28 shows how the long-term durability of a PVC sheet was affected by conditioning for a week at +60°C. The heat treatment increased the yield stress but reduced the ductility.[21-23]

Although the mechanical behaviour is complex, because of these numerous factors, it is possible to design within acceptable limits of accuracy and without undue effort, provided that the critical *practical* parameters can be identified.

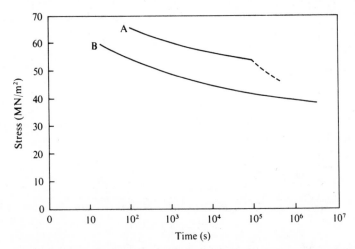

Figure 6.28   Failure stress of PVC at +20°C as a function of time under load. Full lines ductile, dashed line brittle. A. After a week at +60°C. B. As moulded

To a first approximation, density can replace crystallinity in the characterization of crystalline polymers but second-order rules can be evolved when this simplification is too crude.

6.7 MOLECULAR WEIGHT

The molecular weight is determined in the first instance by the choice of the balance between easy processability and good toughness. Thereafter, it is affected by degradation during processing and ageing and perhaps by chemical attack or radiation (ultraviolet, γ-rays, electrons and electric discharges, etc.); these effects can be significantly changed by the use of suitable stabilizers or pro-degradants.

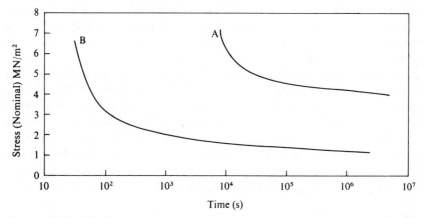

Figure 6.29 Nett breaking stress of double edge notched specimens (razor notches) as a function of time under load at +20°C in 200 cs silicone oil. Low-density polyethylene. A. Melt flow index 0·3. High molecular weight. B. Melt flow index 20. Low molecular weight

Changes in molecular weight have little direct effect on moduli and yield stresses though it is sometimes noted that molecular weight reduction in crystallizable polymers gives higher crystallinity, with the consequent increase in modulus and yield stress.

Increasing molecular weight improves fatigue resistance and reduction in molecular weight tends to promote brittle fracture in impact, fatigue and environmental stress cracking. Figure 6.29 illustrates this by a comparison of two low-density polyethylenes of different molecular weight. Sharply notched specimens were tested under constant load in the presence of a silicone fluid and the superior behaviour of the higher molecular weight polymer (melt flow index 0·3) was very marked.

Too high a molecular weight may cause difficulty in processing and the high viscosity leads to greater anisotropy in mouldings. The disadvantage of anisotropy sometimes outweighs the advantage of high molecular weight with the possible nett result that the higher molecular weight material has inferior service performance.

From a practical point of view, it is necessary to ensure that fracture data used apply to the specific grade of material intended for the application and that the test specimens are prepared from realistic mouldings.

6.8   ORIENTATION AND ANISOTROPY

Molecular orientation can cause profound changes in the mechanical properties of polymers and advantage has been taken of this in the production of oriented synthetic fibres and films. In bulk applications of plastics, orientation is less pronounced and is more usually an unwanted consequence of the fabrication process. The degree of orientation depends on the melt viscosity, the frabrication conditions and the shape of the mould.

Molecular orientation leads to anisotropy of the mechanical properties. Compared with an isotropic moulding, the modulus is increased when a tensile stress is along the principal orientation direction (or melt flow direction) and decreased perpendicular to that direction; certain shear moduli are also decreased. A greater number of tests are needed for the larger number of elastic constants required for full evaluation and reliable calculations in a significantly anisotropic moulding. This involves a great deal of extra work and is not really practicable at present; the required information is not available.

If it can be assumed that tensile stresses are only applied parallel to the orientation direction, then orientation improves modulus, strength and toughness as in fibres and films. However, it is more common with thermoplastics that a tensile stress can equally well be applied perpendicular to the orientation direction. For example, a hammer blow creates a state of biaxial tensile stress, cracks are initiated in the weakest direction and tend to propagate along the flow lines. As discussed in section 5.6, it is necessary, for realistic results, to make impact tests in which the tensile stress is applied perpendicular to the orientation. The same applies to other fracture tests such as tensile and flexural tests, fatigue and environmental stress cracking.

More exaggerated effects are possible with rubbery additives in which the particles become elongated and oriented; Figure 5.12 has already illustrated large effects in ABS. With fibrous additives, the fibres tend to lie along the flow direction and again the anisotropy in both modulus and fracture stress is particularly marked. Figure 6.4 has already illustrated the effect of this type of anisotropy on long-term durability for dry nylon.

Orientation and anisotropy, like the other factors discussed in this chapter, can have an important influence on the results of laboratory tests and on behaviour in service. At best, the designer could arrange to take advantage of the superior properties possible with optimum choice of material, mould design and fabrication conditions. At worst, it is necessary to avoid being misled by arbitrary tests on poorly selected and unrealistic samples.

6.9 REFERENCES

1. S. Turner, 'Data systems for engineering design with polyolefines: manipulations to reduce testing costs', *Plastics and Polymers*, **38**, 282–9 (1970).
2. R. C. Hartlein, 'New coupling concepts for glass-reinforced thermoplastics', *Ind. Engng. Chem. Prod. Res. Dev.*, **10**, No. 1, 92–9 (1972).
3. P. I. Vincent, 'Fracture: Short-term phenomena', *Encyclopaedia of Polymer Science and Technology*, Vol. 7, Wiley, New York, 1967, pp. 292–361.
4. K. V. Gotham, 'Long-term strength of thermoplastics: the ductile–brittle transition in static fatigue', *Plastics and Polymers*, 59–64 (1972).
5. N. T. Hall, 'The effect of glass fibres, coupling agents and compounding procedures on physical properties of nylon, polycarbonate, acetal and other thermoplastics', XXII, *ANTEX*, SPE, Montreal, 1966.
6. J. Dimmock and M. Abrahams, 'Prediction of composite properties from fibre and matrix properties', *Composites*, **1**, 87–93 (1969).
7. V. Heidingsfeld and J. Zelinger, 'Effect of fillers on physicomechanical properties of PVC', Sci. Papers Inst. Chem. Technol., Prague, C12, 1967, p. 71–93.
8. S. S. Pelishenko, I. A. Uskov and V. P. Solomko, 'Change in mechanical properties and water absorption of nylon 6 on addition of fine particle fillers', *Soviet Plastics*, 60 (1966).
9. K. Streib and K. Oberbach, 'Glass-fibre reinforced polycarbonates', *Kunststoffe*, **56**, 15 (1966).
10. A. Wambach, K. Trachte and A. Di Benedetto, 'Fracture properties of glass-filled PPO', *J. Composite Materials*, **2**, 265 (1968).
11. C. B. Bucknall, K. V. Gotham and P. I. Vincent, 'Fracture II—The empirical approach', Chapter 10 in Vol. 1, *Polymer Science* (Ed. A. D. Jenkins), North Holland, 1972.
12. W. J. Jackson and J. R. Caldwell, 'Antiplasticization II', *J. Appl. Poly. Sci.*, **11**, 211 (1967).
13. P. I. Vincent and S. Raha, 'Influence of hydrogen bonding on crazing and cracking of amorphous thermoplastics', *Polymer*, 283–7, (13 June 1972).
14. J. B. Howard, 'Stress-cracking', Chapter 11 in *Engineering Design for Plastics* (Ed. E. Baer), Reinhold, 1964.
15. F. E. Karasz, 'Physical properties of the system: poly(2,6-dimethyl phenylene ether)—polystyrene', American Chemical Society, Division of Polymer Chemistry, Polymer Preprints, **11**, 1 February 1970, p. 357.
16. V. L. Folt, 'Physical properties of ethylene-1-olefin copolymers', *S.P.E. Trans.*, **2**, 285 (1962).
17. T. Huff, 'Copolymers of propylene with -olefines', *J. Appl. Poly. Sci.*, **8**, 825 (1964).
18. K. Fletcher, R. N. Haward and J. Mann, 'Rubber-reinforced polystyrene and copolymers', *Chem. and Ind.*, **45**, 1854 (1965).

19. P. Fischer, 'Testing plastics welds', *Kunststoffe*, **56**, 188 (1966).
20. G. Schonefeld and S. Wintergerst, 'Alterations in structure and strength of polypropylene by heat treatment', *Kunststoffe*, **60**, No. 3, 177–84 (1970).
21. D. M. Gezovich and P. H. Geil, 'Morphology of quenched polypropylene', *Polym. Engng. Sci.*, **8**, 202–210 (1968).
22. K. H. Illers, 'Influence of thermal history on the properties of PVC', *Makromol. Chem.*, **127**, 1–33 (1969).
23. G. Peilstöcker, 'Temperature behaviour of polycarbonate', *Brit. Plast.*, **35**, 35 (1962).

7

Electrical Properties

by K. A. Buckingham

7.1 INTRODUCTION

Electrically, virtually all polymers and most plastics are insulators; these properties derive from, on the one hand, their chemical structure, texture and morphology, and on the other, the properties of any residual process residues, impurities and additives. These properties are essentially independent of electric stress at low stresses, but at high stresses, new, stress-dependent, phenomena occur which frequently affect the performance and life of the materials. A number of special plastics have been developed which fall into either electrically-conducting or antistatic categories;[1] their properties are achieved by the use of particular additives and the polymer is used (electrically) solely as a carrier for the additives.

The first section of this chapter deals with the properties of 'insulating plastics' in terms of (a) properties at low electric stress, and (b) properties at high electric stress. The second section deals with electrostatic phenomena that are associated with the use of these insulating materials, and the properties of antistatic and electrically-conducting grades.

7.2 ELECTRICAL PROPERTIES AT LOW STRESS

Along with other more traditional insulating materials the bulk properties of plastics may be fairly precisely described in terms of a temperature- and frequency-dependent permittivity (dielectric constant) and power factor (loss tangent), and a temperature- and time-dependent volume resistivity. These terms are usually defined[2] in the following manner:

(1) Permittivity (ε'). The ratio of the capacitance C_x, of a given configuration of electrodes, with a material as a dielectric, to the capacitance, C_v, of the same configuration of electrodes with a vacuum as the dielectric.

$$\varepsilon' = \frac{C_x}{C_v} \tag{7.1}$$

(2) Power Factor (loss tangent, loss angle). The ratio of the power dissipated in a material to the product of the effective applied, sinusoidal voltage and current. Numerically, it is equal to the cosine of the angular difference between the applied sinusoidal voltage (V) and the component of the resulting current (I) having the same frequency, e.g.

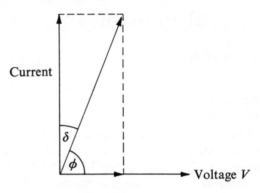

$$\text{Power Factor} = \frac{\text{Dissipated power in watts}}{\text{Applied voltage} \times \text{resulting current}} = \cos \phi$$

as $\phi \to 90°$, $\cos \phi \to \tan \delta$ which is known as the loss tangent.

As the loss tangent of plastics material may be anywhere in the range $\tan \delta = 0.000005$ to 0.3, for convenience it is usual to describe the lower part of this range in angular units (loss angle in micro-radians, μrad) since

$$\text{as } \delta \to 0, \tan \delta \to \delta \text{ in radians};$$
$$1 \ \mu\text{rad} = 0.000001 \text{ in } \tan \delta \text{ units}$$

(3) Volume Resistivity (ρ). The ratio of the potential gradient parallel to the direction of the current flow in the material to the current density. It is measured in units of ohm-metre, and is numerically equal to the volume resistance in ohms between opposite faces of a 1 metre cube of material. It is dependent on the time of electrification.

The surface properties are usually described in terms of 'surface resistivity' which, theoretically, is the ratio of the potential gradient parallel to the direction of current flow along its surface to the current per unit width of the surface. It is quoted in units of ohms, and is numerically equal to the surface resistance between two electrodes forming opposite sides of a square. The size of the square is immaterial, and hence occasionally the units are given as ohm/square.

7.2.1 Loss Tangent and Permittivity

There are three basic mechanisms that give rise to dielectric loss in polymers,[3, 4, 5] within the frequency range covered by electrical engineers. These are described as (i) dipolar, (ii) interfacial polarization losses, and (iii) loss arising from conduction currents.

Firstly, in the dipolar type, dielectric loss is caused by the interaction of permanent electric dipoles, which arise from the asymmetry of the electrical charges in the molecules, with the applied electric field. For any one species of

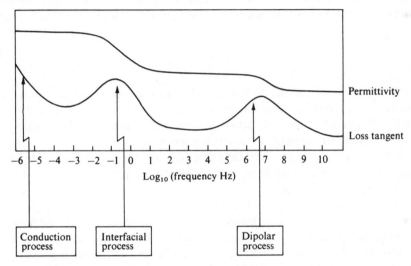

Figure 7.1 Curves of loss and permittivity vs. $\log_{10}$ frequency

dipole, the loss tangent of the material will vary with frequency as shown in Figure 7.1. The frequency at which the loss tangent is a maximum is known as the relaxation frequency. The number and amplitude of individual processes that are exhibited in any one material will depend on the number of species and dipoles present in the material, their concentration and dipole moments, and their possible separate or co-operative motions.

Interfacial processes, which mostly occur at frequencies $<10^6$ Hz, are exhibited by two- or multi-component systems where one of the components, usually the polymer, behaves essentially as a dielectric and the other component as a conductor. The system therefore looks like a resistance/capacitance matrix and loss is caused by charge redistribution with the reversal of the alternating field. The relaxation frequency of the mechanism is dependent on the properties of the two individual components and also on the nature of their physical distribution, e.g. spherical droplets or say fibre-shape particles in the plastic. The following equation gives an approximate guide to the frequency of maximum absorption:

$$f_{max} = 1\cdot8 \times 10^{12} \frac{\sigma_2}{2\varepsilon_1' + \varepsilon_2'} \tag{7.2}$$

where ε_1' is the permittivity of the insulating phase; ε_2' is the permittivity of the second phase; σ_2 is the conductivity of the second phase.

Lastly, when a plastic contains free-charge carriers, i.e. ions or electrons, it may exhibit a conduction current in phase with an applied electric field which will give rise to dielectric loss, the magnitude of which varies inversely with frequency (Figure 7.1), according to equation (7.3) where C is the effective

$$\tan \delta = \frac{1}{\omega CR} \tag{7.3}$$

capacitance of the specimen, R is the effective resistance, and $\omega = 2\pi \times$ frequency. This type of process usually occurs at very low frequencies, <100 Hz, and is frequently found in naturally occurring materials, occasionally in plastics, but rarely in polymers at room temperature.

It can, therefore, be seen that the curve of loss tangent versus frequency for any plastic material is likely to have a complex shape; its level may in fact range over a few decades.

Polymers are broadly classified into two groups, polar and non-polar, i.e. those in which the basic polymer repeat unit contains strong unbalanced dipoles, and those in which the polymer chain is more balanced or contains only a low concentration of weak dipoles. The losses of polar materials are mostly in the range $\tan \delta = 0\cdot001$ to $0\cdot3$, and of non-polar materials from a few micro-radians up to approximately 1000 μrad ($\tan \delta = 0\cdot001$).

At very high frequencies, or at frequencies above all the significant loss processes, the permittivity of a material is approximately equal to the square of its optical refractive index. As the frequency is reduced, the value of permittivity increases as each succeeding polarization, dipolar or interfacial, adds its contribution ($\Delta\varepsilon'$) with the result that the permittivity reaches its highest value at zero frequency (Figure 7.1). For non-polar materials, where $\Delta\varepsilon'$ is small, the permittivity is essentially independent of frequency and is related to the density by the Clausius–Mosotti equation (7.4).

$$\frac{\varepsilon' - 1}{\varepsilon' + 2} = k\rho \tag{7.4}$$

where $\varepsilon' = $ permittivity; $\rho = $ density; $k = $ a material constant $= 0\cdot325$ for LD polyethylene, $0\cdot325$ for polypropylene, $0\cdot119$ for PTFE and $0\cdot329$ for poly-4-methyl-pentene.

Figure 7.2 gives loss tangent and permittivity curves as a function of frequency at room temperature for a plastic, and illustrates a typical sigmoidal transition in the value of the permittivity that occurs with a relaxation loss process.

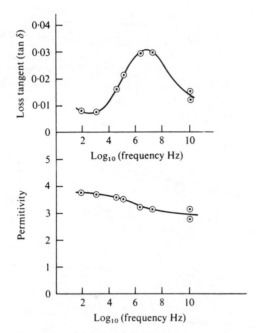

Figure 7.2 Permittivity and loss curves for a polar material

Loss processes approximately obey activated rate process theory with activation energies in the range up to 100 kcal/mole, and loss tangent values are therefore markedly dependent on temperature. For non-polar materials, permittivity, on the other hand, only changes with temperature because the density changes due to thermal expansion; for polar types the changes are somewhat larger as they include a further contribution arising from the change in loss level.[6]

Typically, data are published in the form of contour maps with temperature and frequency as ordinate and abscissa.[7] By way of illustration, Figure 7.3 shows a contour map of the loss tangent for an electrical-grade planar-oriented polyethylene terephthalate film and Figure 7.4 shows, for the same material, curves of loss tangent as a function of frequency at two constant temperatures. These curves have been derived from the contour maps. The corresponding permittivity map for the film is given in Figure 7.5. As an

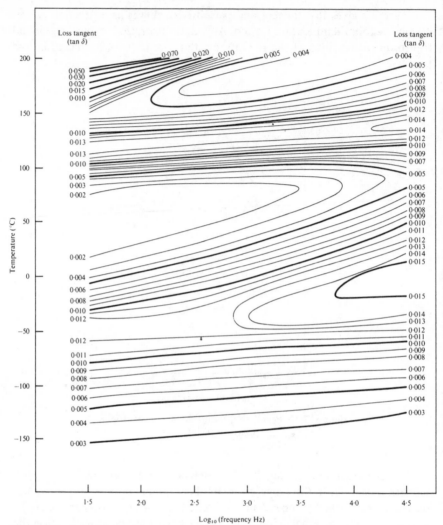

Figure 7.3   Variation of loss tangent with temperature and frequency. Polyethylene terephthalate planar-oriented film [Melinex]

example of a non-polar material, the loss curve for a low-density polyethylene is given in Figure 7.6 for 23°C.

An important factor in the development of materials for electrical application is the proper selection of those additives, necessary for thermal stability, colour or strength, etc., so that the dielectric loss level is retained at a level as close as possible to that of the virgin material.[8, 9]

Figure 7.7 shows dielectric loss curves for a natural low-density polyethylene, a red compound based on the same polymer, and another red compound again

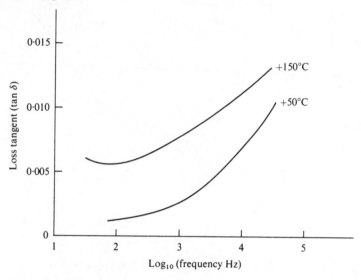

Figure 7.4 Variation of loss tangent with frequency at constant temperature for Melinex film

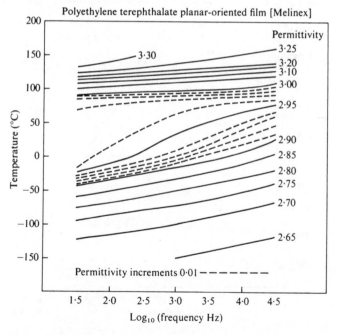

Figure 7.5 Variation of permittivity with temperature and frequency

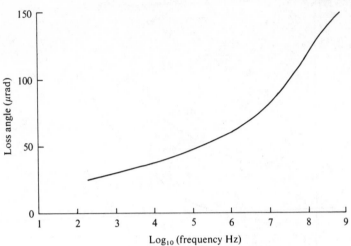

Figure 7.6   Dielectric losses of 0·934 density polyethylene

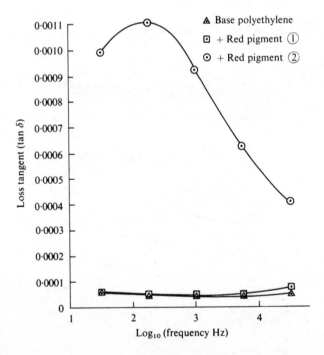

Figure 7.7   The effect of pigment formulation on the dielectric losses of polyethylene

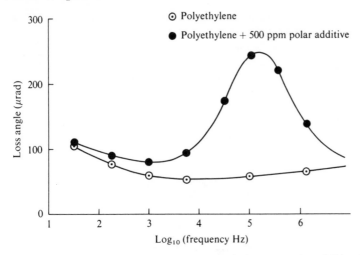

Figure 7.8 The effect of a small concentration of a polar additive on dielectric loss

based on the same polymer, but in this instance using an unsatisfactory pigment formulation. As the proportional effect of any polar additive or impurity must depend on the concentration of dipoles in the polymer itself, it therefore follows that the problems arising from additives and contaminants occur mainly with the non-polar materials: even a few parts per million can have significant effects as can be seen, for example, in Figure 7.8.

7.2.2 Volume Resistivity

In the standard experimental procedure for the measurement of resistivity, a direct voltage is applied across the specimen and the resulting current measured in some convenient manner. Figure 7.9 shows the shape of the resulting current time curves for a pure, ideal dielectric, for a dielectric in which the permittivity itself is a function of time and frequency and, lastly, for a dielectric that also contains a number of mobile charge carriers. Plastics materials fall into this third category although the level of the conduction current varies markedly from material to material and may also itself decay with time if the number of charge carriers is limited. The corresponding resistivity curves have a shape that is the inverse of these current time curves and resistivity is therefore markedly time-dependent. In general, very few plastics show true conduction behaviour at room temperature, but the chance of conduction occurring is increased at elevated temperatures and by the presence of ionic impurities.[10] Although low values of resistivity will give rise to correspondingly high values of $\tan\delta$ according to equation (7.3), the converse is not true and, indeed, plastics exhibiting some of the lowest levels of conduction current are polar materials with $\tan\delta$ values $\sim 0\cdot01$.

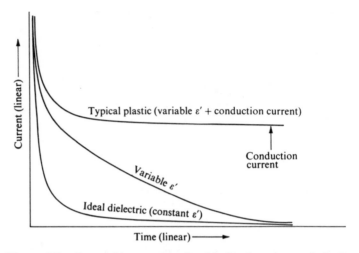

Figure 7.9 Current/time curves for idealized and practical dielectrics

Frequently, the value of the volume resistivity, measured one minute after the electrification of the specimen, is quoted for materials. There is no implication however, in these cases, that it has reached an equilibrium, i.e. a time-independent level. The practice has arisen because of a British Standard requirement[11] which, in the majority of cases, is only of value for quality-control purposes.

7.2.3 Surface Resistivity and Insulation Resistance

The surface resistivity of a material is dependent upon its polarity and is also linked to its hydrophobic or hydrophilic character, its surface profile and the type and degree of contamination of that surface. The nature of the environment also affects behaviour. The results of measurements made on clean laboratory specimens and using standard test methods[12] are often quoted. Care must be taken when assessing the usefulness of a material in this context because of the major effects of contamination and humidity.

Insulation resistance test methods are standardized:[13, 14] basically they refer to the resistance between two electrodes fixed into an insulator, and therefore depend on the volume and surface resistivity of the specimen.

7.3 ELECTRICAL PROPERTIES AT HIGH STRESS

In the first part of this chapter it was possible to discuss the inherent properties of insulating plastics, which are virtually independent of the geometry of the material and associated conductors except for the effects of surface leakage. As the electric stress level is raised, however, the physical arrangement of the dielectric and conductors becomes increasingly important and at very high stresses only the direct results of experiments on particular assemblies can be reported usefully.

It will be appreciated, therefore, that whereas at low stresses the values of the electrical parameters of materials may be used directly by design engineers, at intermediate and high stresses the results of standardized tests and of research only serve as an approximate guide to the choice of material and to design; the actual performance of the real assembly must be finally proved.

When a dielectric/conductor combination is subject to an increasing electric stress in the absence of electrical discharges, the effect may be to cause a new set of thermal equilibrium conditions to be set up, or alternatively, to produce runaway behaviour resulting in electrical breakdown and destruction of the insulating material. The dependence of the three basic mechanisms for dielectric loss on temperature was described in the first part of this chapter. Even though the dipolar contribution is generally independent of stress levels, the actual power dissipation in a dielectric is proportional to the frequency and the square of the electric field; therefore the temperature of the dielectric will increase with increasing stress levels; this effect may be self-stabilizing if the dipolar loss level falls with increasing temperature. However, the increase in temperature will change the magnitude and frequency of any interfacial loss processes and increase the level of conduction. The sum of these effects may be to increase yet again the power dissipation and thereby raise the temperature of the material above the safe working limit, producing overall mechanical failure, chemical destruction or electrical breakdown. Heating effects may, however, be beneficial and use is made of radio-frequency dielectric heating in the plastics fabrication industry.

However, with many plastic materials, failure occurs from the effects of internal or external electrical (spark) discharges before the onset of failure by thermal runaway, either by the production of conducting tracks through or on the surface of the material, or by erosion. A more detailed discussion of the mechanisms underlying the failure from discharges is the subject of more specialized treatment,[3, 15, 16] and it is sufficient to point out here that the life of any component will be very dependent on both the rate and magnitude of the discharges and, therefore, on the electric stress levels at the conductor surfaces, the field distribution, the size and nature of inhomogeneities in the material, such as voids, contamination both in the material and on its surface,

Table 7.1

Subject of test	Test method No. and title	
Dielectric breakdown voltage and dielectric strength at power frequencies	BS 2918	Electric Strength of Solid Insulating Materials at Power Frequencies
	ASTM D149	Dielectric Breakdown Voltage and Dielectric Strength of Electrical Insulating Materials at Commercial Power Frequencies
	ASTM D.2305	Testing Polymeric Films used for Electrical Insulation
	IEC 243	Recommended Methods of Test for Electric Strength of Solid Insulating Materials at Power Frequencies
	VDE 0303 PT.2	Determination of the Electrical Breakdown Voltage and the Electric Strength at Power Frequencies
Relative resistance of materials to breakdown by surface discharges	ASTM 2275	Test for Voltage Endurance under Corona Attack of Solid Electrical Insulating Materials
	IEC 343	Recommended Test Methods for Determining the Relative Resistance of Insulating Materials to Breakdown by Surface Discharges
	VDE 0303 PT.7	Determination of Behaviour under Corona Discharge
Comparative tracking index	BS 3781	Method for Determining the Comparative Tracking Index of Solid Insulating Materials
	IEC 112	Recommended Method for Determining the Comparative Tracking Index of Solid Insulating Materials under Moist Conditions
	VDE 0303 PT.1	Determination of Tracking Resistance Operating at Voltages of up to 1000 V
Inclined plane tracking and erosion	Revision of BS 3840	Polyester Dough Moulding Compounds
	ASTM 2303	Test for Liquid Contaminant, Inclined Plane Tracking and Erosion of Insulating Materials
Differential wet tracking	ASTM 2302	Test for Differential Wet Tracking Resistance of Electrical Insulating materials with Controlled Water to Metal Discharges
Dust and fog tracking and erosion	ASTM 2132	Test for Dust and Fog Tracking and Erosion Resistance of Electrical Insulating Materials
Arc resistance high voltage, low current	ASTM 495	High Voltage, Low Current Arc Resistance of Solid Electrical Insulating Materials
	VDE 0303 PT.5	Determination of Arc Resistance
Fusewire arc test	BS 3497	Unimpregnated Asbestos Cement Boards (Incombustible) for Electrical Purposes

the shape of the insulator and conductors, the environment and the external circuit. Ideally, designers should aim for complete freedom from discharges in assemblies where long life is required.

A number of destructive and non-destructive tests have been standardized, by which the life and behaviour of materials may be assessed under specific conditions. The destructive types are mostly only short time tests and as such are more useful for product quality control than for design purposes where component lives in excess of ten years are frequently required. Attempts to assess the effect of the type of surface contamination that occurs on outdoor insulation systems and of the circuit parameters are made in other tests. A list of standard test methods commonly used to assess materials is given in Table 7.1.

7.4 ELECTROSTATIC PHENOMENA AND ANTISTATIC PLASTICS

The presence of electrostatic charge in or on a material is usually recognized by mutual attraction or repulsion between it and other surfaces accompanied by, in some instances, small spark discharges, or by a high rate of dust pick-up. In powders it may significantly change the flow properties. The existence of these phenomena in plastics is not surprising in view of the very high values of volume and surface resistivity that are often exhibited; their occurrence is mostly irritating, occasionally useful as, for example, in copying machines, but can also lead to dangerous situations.

The effects may be alleviated by neutralizing the charge: i.e. by supplying a charge of opposite sign at the appropriate rate; by purposely reducing the surface resistivity so that either the charge leaks away, or at least spreads out so that it has a large capacitance to earth and thereby has a lower potential; or by isolating and eliminating the mechanism producing the charge.

In applications where the phenomena give rise to effects that are solely irritating and not hazardous, such as, for example, dust pick-up on plastic bottles and surfaces, charge on carpets, etc., it is usually sufficient either to apply a hygroscopic coating to the surface or to incorporate an antistatic additive in the plastic which will migrate to the polymer surface and produce a surface with low values of surface resistivity.

In cases where a spark discharge could lead to a hazardous situation, as for example in the presence of flammable vapours or powders with low ignition energy, more certain methods are desirable. This requirement has led to the production of antistatic plastics[1] in which low values of volume as well as surface resistivity are obtained by the use of additives. With this type of product, the provision of a high relative humidity in the local environment is not necessary.

7.5 ELECTRICALLY CONDUCTING PLASTICS

These are mostly produced by incorporating high concentrations of filamentary carbon black or certain pyrolized compounds into otherwise insulating materials. Their electrical properties are usually described adequately in terms of volume and surface resistivity. The properties, which rely on the mesh work of carbon filaments, may depend on fabrication methods and may also change with mechanical flexing and contact pressure.

7.6 REFERENCES

1. British Standard No. 2050, 1961, *Specification for Electrical Resistance of Conductive and Antistatic Products made from Flexible Polymeric Material.*
2. American Society for Testing and Materials (ASTM) Test No. D.150, 1965, *A–C Loss Characteristics and Dielectric Constant (Permittivity) of Solid Electrical Insulating Materials.*
3. J. B. Birks and J. H. Schulman, *Progress in Dielectrics Series*, Vols. 1 and 3, Heywood, 1959 and 1961.
4. J. C. Anderson, *Dielectrics*, Chapman & Hall, 1964.
5. J. B. Birks, *Modern Dielectric Materials*, Heywood, 1960.
6. W. Reddish, 'Chemical structure and dielectric properties of polymers', *Pure and Appl. Chem.*, **5** (1962).
7. W. Reddish, 'The dielectric properties of polyethylene terephthalate', *Trans. Faraday Soc.*, **46** (1950).
8. I. T. Barrie, K. A. Buckingham, W. Reddish, 'Dielectric properties of polythene for submarine telephone cables', *Proc. IEE*, **113**, No. 11 (1966).
9. K. A. Buckingham, and W. Reddish, 'Low loss polypropylene for electrical purposes', *Proc. IEE*, **114**, No. 11 (1967).
10. W. Reddish, 'Conduction and polarization in plasticized PVC compounds', *Soc. Chem. Ind. Symp.*, Mar. 1958.
11. British Standard 2782, *Methods of Testing Plastics*, Method 202, Volume Resistivity.
12. British Standard 2782, *Methods of Testing Plastics*, Method 203A, Surface Resistivity.
13. British Standard 2782, *Methods of Testing Plastics*, Method 204, Insulation Resistance.
14. ASTM D.257, *D–C Resistance or Conductance of Insulating Materials.*
15. F. H. Kreuger, *Discharge Detection in HV Equipment*, Heywood, 1964.
16. L. L. Alstan, *High Voltage Technology*, Oxford Univ. Press, 1968.

8

Thermal Properties

by A. W. Birley and D. C. F. Couzens

8.1 INTRODUCTION

The study of thermal properties embraces crystalline melting point, heat content (enthalpy), thermal expansion and thermal conductivity, which are essentially equilibrium properties in the sense that, unlike properties discussed in earlier chapters, time is not an important variable. This chapter also discusses transition temperatures, which are time-dependent in some degree, and the transient phenomena involved in heat transfer. The thermal properties under consideration are not strict materials' constants, since they are dependent to some extent on temperature and, like the properties considered in earlier chapters, on the previous thermal history of the sample and on other factors. Information on the effect of temperature on mechanical properties has been considered as temperature effect on the appropriate properties. Thus, test procedures such as deflection temperature under load[1,2] and brittleness temperature[3] are aspects of deformation behaviour and impact strength respectively.

8.2 CRYSTALLINE MELTING POINT

It has been noted in Chapter 2 that the molecular chains of certain polymers can form into ordered regions, i.e. crystallites, and that these have a marked effect on materials' properties. It is not unexpected, therefore, that the melting of the crystallites affects the properties of a partially crystalline polymer and that the temperature at which this occurs sets an upper limit to the working range of crystalline plastics. At the same time, the crystalline melting point is generally the lower limit for plastics processing, although for a molten plastics material the crystallization temperature is generally considerably lower than the crystalline melting point; this effect is known as supercooling.

The crystallites of plastics materials vary in size and perfection, depending on local variations in molecular structure, such as chain branching, and on the thermal history of the sample. For these reasons, the melting of the crystallites is not a single catastrophic phenomenon occurring over a narrow temperature range, as is the case for crystals of low molecular weight organic compounds, but is a process which takes place progressively with increasing temperature. The melting range may extend over many tens of degrees: typically a range of some 75°C is quoted for low-density polyethylene (final melting point 115°C) although the effect on properties is not particularly serious until a temperature of 75°C is reached. The corresponding melting range for polypropylene with a final melting temperature of 170°C is 10–20°C, whilst nylon 66 has a narrow melting range of only 3–5°C. The temperature at which the last traces of crystallinity disappear is the absolute upper limit for form stability and is the temperature usually quoted.

Measurements of crystalline melting point and melting range can be made by a variety of techniques, the most direct of which is monitoring the crystallinity by X-ray diffraction as the temperature of the sample is increased. Other techniques measuring crystallinity-dependent properties are usually employed for their greater convenience: methods such as birefringence and differential scanning calorimetry are widely used. It is not usually possible to obtain information on the temperature dependence of crystallinity from methods used for examining crystals of low molecular weight organic compounds, such as, for example, melting point tubes.

8.3   HEAT CONTENT (ENTHALPY)

The amount of heat required to change the temperature of a sample between specified limits is the product of its mass and the *enthalpy*, or *heat content per unit mass*. Thus enthalpy is defined as the total amount of heat required to change the temperature of unit mass of material from one temperature to another. The data are usually based on a reference temperature of 20°C and presented as curves of enthalpy vs. temperature from this reference base. The quantity of heat required to raise the temperature of a sample by one degree is its *thermal capacity* but for the comparison of materials it is conventional to quote values of thermal capacity of unit mass, also known as the *specific heat*. In the ideal case of a material with a constant specific heat, the enthalpy is the product of the specific heat and the rise in temperature.

When heat is supplied at a steady rate to a pure crystalline solid, the temperature rises steadily at a rate depending on the specific heat until a definite temperature, the melting point, is reached. At this stage, no further rise in temperature is observed until melting has taken place, all the thermal energy being absorbed in destroying the regular arrangement in the crystals. When melting is complete the temperature of the liquid increases steadily as heat is supplied, at a rate corresponding to the specific heat of the liquid. The heat required to melt unit mass of crystalline material to a liquid at the same temperature is the *latent heat of fusion*.

In principle it is possible, therefore, to quantify the behaviour of a material by four constants, as indicated in Figure 8.1:

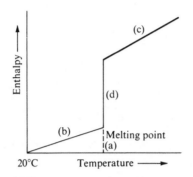

Figure 8.1 Schematic plot of enthalpy versus temperature for crystalline material

(a) the melting point;
(b) enthalpy from 20°C to melting point (or the specific heat of the solid);
(c) enthalpy from melting point to higher reference temperatures (or the specific heat of the liquid);
(d) latent heat of fusion at the melting point.

Irrespective of the shape of the enthalpy-temperature curve, the enthalpy referred to a base at 20°C is given at any other temperature by reading directly from the curve. This type of enthalpy vs. temperature plot is a preferred method for presentation of enthalpy data. An example of such a curve for a simple organic crystalline solid is given in Figure 8.2.[4]

This simple picture does not apply to polymers because, as we have noted in section 8.2, even partially crystalline materials do not have sharp melting points and similarity of the enthalpy vs. temperature curves for polymers to Figures 8.1 and 8.2 is not immediately obvious. Such curves for a crystalline and an amorphous polymer are given in Figures 8.3 and 8.4, respectively. In Figure 8.3 the crystallites melt progressively as the temperature is increased, giving increasing curvature to the enthalpy vs. temperature plot up to the melting point. The construction shows the relationship to Figure 8.1. It can be seen that the concept of specific heat as a constant for the solid material (specific heat is the slope of the enthalpy vs. temperature curve), is not tenable for plastics, giving further support to the presentation of enthalpy data as enthalpy vs. temperature plots.

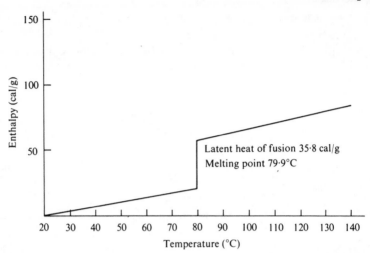

Figure 8.2 Enthalpy vs. temperature data for naphthalene (after M. E. Spaght, S. B. Thomas and G. S. Parks, *J. Phys. Chem.*, **36**, 882 (1932))

For amorphous plastics, the enthalpy vs. temperature curve (Figure 8.4) changes slope, i.e. there is a step change in specific heat, in the glass–rubber transition temperature region, although the change may be a gradual one. This provides one of the established methods for determining T_g, the glass–rubber transition temperature referred to below.

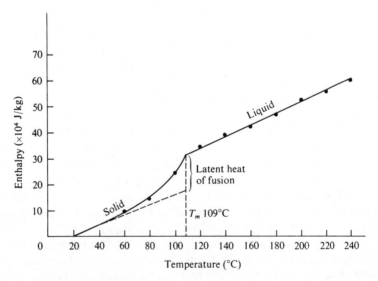

Figure 8.3 Enthalpy vs. temperature: low-density polyethylene

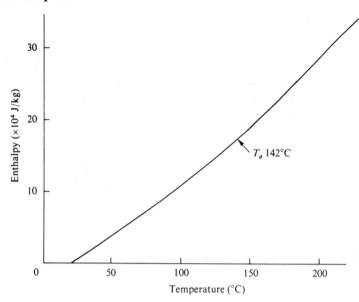

Figure 8.4 Enthalpy data for polycarbonate, (after J. M. O'Reilly, F. E. Karasz and H. E. Bair, *J. Poly. Sci. C*, No. 6, 109 (1963))

An understanding of enthalpy is essential to an appreciation of transient thermal phenomena, such as thermal diffusivity and temperature–crystallization relationships and provides a measure of the energy requirement for the heating and cooling of plastics in processing operations.

8.3.1 The Glass–Rubber Transition Temperature

The glass–rubber transition was considered in Chapter 2 and whilst it is less of a material constant than the crystalline melting point (section 8.2), nevertheless it frequently represents the upper working temperature limit for non-crystalline plastics. Various methods can be used for its determination, the commonest being:

(a) inflection in the plot of heat content vs. temperature curve (i.e. step change in specific heat);

(b) inflection in the plot of specific volume (or its reciprocal, density) vs. temperature;

(c) abrupt change in modulus, frequently associated with softening point for which there are many standard methods such as Deflection Temperature under Load and indentation Vicat Softening Temperature.

8.3.1.1 *Change in Specific Heat*

A very easy determination of T_g can be made with the recently developed differential thermal equipment. Two basic designs of instrument are available.

(1) Differential scanning calorimeter. A temperature increasing linearly with time is maintained in two sample cells, one containing the test substance and the other a reference material which does not have any transitions in the

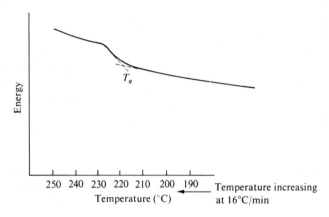

Figure 8.5   D. S. C. trace for polyethersulphone. $T_g = 218°C$

temperature region of interest. The energy inputs to the two cells necessary to maintain equal temperatures are compared, and the out-of-balance recorded. Thus exothermic and endothermic processes are recorded as maxima and minima and a change in specific heat as a change in base line of the record. This is exemplified in Figure 8.5 for a polyethersulphone.[6]

Polyethersulphone

(2) Differential thermal analysis. In this technique, heat is supplied equally to two cells, one containing the test substance and the other an inert reference material. Temperature differences between the two cells resulting from thermal processes are recorded.

These two differential thermal techniques have largely replaced traditional adiabatic calorimetry for the determination of T_g but the older, more laborious method is still required for accurate enthalpy or specific heat measurements.

8.3.1.2 *Specific Volume vs. Temperature Measurements*

Classically these measurements were used to define T_g and they still serve to illustrate transition phenomena most broadly. Figure 8.6 shows specific volume vs. temperature data for polyvinyl chloride. The very marked similarity

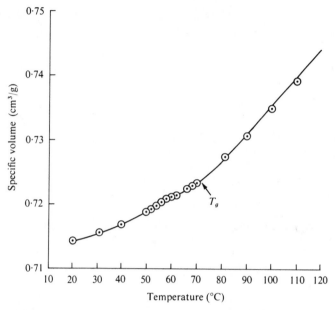

Figure 8.6 Specific volume vs. temperature: PVC (unplasticized)

in the shape of the specific volume vs. temperature and the enthalpy vs. temperature curves especially for crystalline plastics is to be noted. This is a point made by other authors[7] and is shown by comparing Figure 8.7 (for polypropylene) with the enthalpy vs. temperature plot in Figure 8.3 (for polyethylene).

The reader is referred to standard texts for details of these dilatometry measurements but briefly, the volume of a plastics specimen is measured as a function of temperature as the temperature is increased or decreased progressively.

8.3.1.3 *Change in Modulus: Softening Point*

The change in modulus with temperature has been considered in Chapter 3: data for polymethyl methacrylate[8] are given in Figure 8.8 and show the typical catastrophic decrease in modulus occurring at T_g for an amorphous polymer. With such a change in magnitude, it is clear that only comparatively crude apparatus is required to detect the softening point and a variety of tests has

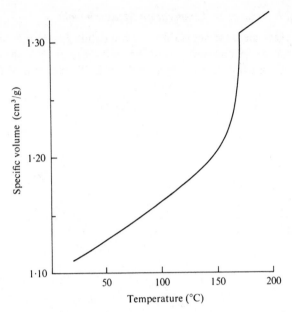

Figure 8.7 Specific volume vs. temperature: polypropylene

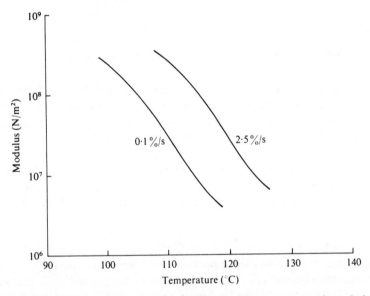

Figure 8.8 Tangent modulus at origin vs. temperature: polymethyl
methacrylate (Perspex) (after K. Deutsch, E. A. W. Hoff and
W. Reddish, *J. Poly. Sci.*, **13**, 565 (1954))

been developed. Typical of these is the Vicat Softening Point test[5] in which the indentation into the specimen of a loaded cylindrical needle of 1 mm² cross-sectional area is measured as the temperature is increased linearly with time. Rapid penetration of the specimen occurs on softening and the softening point is arbitrarily defined as the temperature at which 1 mm penetration is achieved.

In all measurements of T_g, the result obtained depends on the effective *timescale* of the test, that is, on the rate of heating for methods 8.3.1.1 and 8.3.1.2 and the time of loading in a modulus determination. For dynamic modulus measurements where the loading cycle is very short, considerably higher T_g values are observed. This is explained by T_g being associated with relaxation, longer times being required at lower temperatures for the polymer structure to react to the new stress or strain imposed. The effect of strain rate is shown in Figure 8.8, the higher straining rate corresponding to a higher measured transition temperature.

8.3.2 Supercooling

Curves such as those presented in Figures 8.3 and 8.4 are by no means equilibrium curves in that they are not necessarily reversible with respect to heating and cooling cycles although reversibility is more nearly applicable to amorphous plastics (Figure 8.4) than to crystalline materials. The enthalpy vs. temperature curves for amorphous polymers depend on the heating (or cooling) rate and, for solid plastics, the heating curve is affected by the previous thermal history of the sample. For crystalline plastics, the heating and cooling curves are markedly different as all plastics supercool to some extent, so that even if the material is returned to approximately its initial condition (same crystallinity, equivalent thermal history), its enthalpy vs. temperature curve will be markedly different for the heating and cooling cycles. This is shown diagrammatically in Figure 8.9: a crystalline plastics material at O, 20°C is heated to its melting point A, and subsequently in the liquid state to L. The enthalpy vs. temperature relationship follows the path OAL as indicated. On cooling the material L to A there is no departure from the (liquid) enthalpy curve at A, but LA continues to lower temperatures; supercooling is occurring and may persist for many tens of degrees below A, persisting to lower temperatures at higher rates of cooling (C compared with B) where, for the highest rates of cooling, the original starting material O is not regained. The extent of persistence of curve LA to temperatures below the melting point also depends to some extent on the temperature reached along AL and the time the material resides in the melt. If only short times in the melt are involved and particularly if the temperature has only reached 10–20°C above the melting point, crystallite nuclei persist in the melt and are available as the melt is cooled below A,

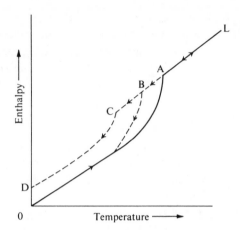

Figure 8.9   Schematic plots of enthalpy versus
temperature for heating and cooling cycles

the melting point, in which case the supercooling effect is less marked but is
present nevertheless.

Curves such as those sketched in Figure 8.9 are difficult to obtain experimentally, but enthalpy data for temperature ranges covering the molten and
solid states are increasingly available: the particular state of quench cooling
is appropriate to the thermal conditions pertaining to the cooling inherent
in many plastics processing operations. For example, the following data
have been obtained for low-density polyethylene over the temperature range
20–140°C:

Heating of solid stored for 3 months at room temperature—389 kJ/kg
Quench cooling of liquid   —368 kJ/kg

Supercooling is most important in all processing operations for crystalline
thermoplastics: the conditions for crystallization largely control the cooling
cycle and some knowledge of the propensity to supercool and a comparison
of the magnitudes involved is important in materials and machine selection
for the fabricator. Differential thermal methods are important since cooling
rates comparable to those achieved in conventional processing operations can
be imposed. Figures 8.10 (a) and (b) show typical data for polypropylene,[9]
for heating and cooling runs respectively. Supercooling is always shown by
plastics which are crystalline in the solid state: however, the magnitude of the
effect depends on molecular factors, molecular weight, molecular weight
distribution and the ease of crystallization (steric effects), and on the rate of
cooling. It can also be reduced by the effect of nucleating additives which
provide heterogeneous nuclei on which the plastics melt can crystallize.

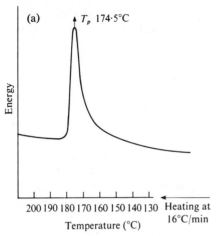

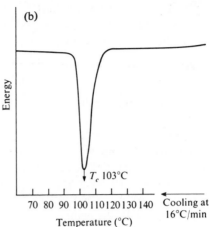

Figure 8.10 (a) Heating curve for polypropylene (previously cooled at 16°C/ min

Figure 8.10 (b) Cooling curve for polypropylene sample as (a) heated to 230°C for 5 min, thereafter cooled at 16°C/min

8.4 THERMAL CONDUCTIVITY

The conduction of heat by solid materials varies widely, values for thermal conductivity ranging over four orders of magnitude with the well-conducting metals such as copper at one extreme and insulating foams (expanded polystyrene, etc.) and fibrous insulations (slag wool) at the other extreme with solid plastics an order of magnitude more conductive. Representative data are given in Table 8.1.

Table 8.1

Material	Thermal conductivity at 20°C, W/m°C (Jm/m² s°C)
Copper	385
Aluminium	240
Mild steel	50
Crown glass	~0·9
Acetal copolymer	0·2
Polypropylene	0·2
Expanded polystyrene (Relative density 0·025)	0·03

The thermal conductivity of a solid plastics material depends on the crystallinity of the material (and, therefore, on the previous thermal history) since the thermal conductivity of the crystallites is considerably greater than that of the amorphous material. This is shown by comparing the thermal conductivity of low-density polyethylene with that of the more crystalline analogue, high-density polyethylene.

LDPE (usually 50% crystallinity) 0.33 W/m°C
HDPE (usually 80% crystallinity) 0.50 W/m°C

Thermal conductivity is also affected by anisotropy in the sample and, where anisotropy exists, it is recommended that appropriate additional measurements be made.

Thermal conductivity measurements are usually made by standard classical steady-state methods: data are usually quoted for specific temperatures of the hot and cold faces appropriate to a variety of established application areas. The water content of the material may affect the result and data are usually given for dry samples.

To solve problems in steady-state heat transfer, i.e. where the temperature at any point does not change with time, one can use Fourier's law of heat conduction. The formulation of the law is straightforward for simple geometric shapes, e.g. flow of heat perpendicular to the faces of a flat slab

$$q = \frac{A\kappa\Delta\theta}{2R} \tag{8.1}$$

where q is the rate of flow of heat; κ is thermal conductivity; A is area; $\Delta\theta$ is temperature difference between the two faces; $2R$ is thickness of slab.

Similarly, the heat flow through the walls of a plastic pipe or of a wire coating is given by:

$$q = \frac{2\pi L\kappa\Delta\theta}{\ln(R_2/R_1)} \tag{8.2}$$

where L is length of cylinder; R_2 and R_1 are external and internal radii of the cylinder, respectively.

In practice, however, the transfer of heat is seldom accomplished by conduction alone, and surface heat transfer effects due to convection and radiation need to be taken into account. For example, heat transferred from the interior of a building to the outside arrives by convection and radiation at the inside surface of the wall, is conducted through the various layers of building material and arrives at the outside surface where it is dissipated to the cold surroundings by convection and radiation (Figure 8.11). In this case the rate of heat loss (q) is given by

$$\frac{q}{A} = \frac{\theta_i - \theta_o}{\dfrac{1}{h_i} + \dfrac{1}{\kappa_a/2R_a} + \dfrac{1}{\kappa_b/2R_b} + \dfrac{1}{h_o}} \tag{8.3}$$

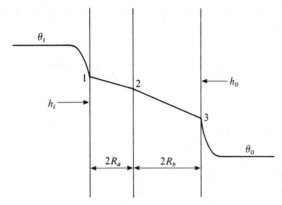

Figure 8.11 Heat conduction through two layers of
material

where h_i and h_0 are the surface heat transfer coefficients due to the combined effects of convection and radiation at the inside and outside surface respectively.

A simple example of this is heat loss through a 'Perspex' window. A room at a controlled temperature of 21°C has a 'Perspex' window 6 mm thick. Outside the temperature is 4°C and a wind is blowing at 15 mph. The heat loss per unit area of window is required. The thermal conductivity of 'Perspex' is 0·19 W/m°C, $h_i = 10$ W/m²°C and h_0 at a wind speed of 15 mph is 35 W/m²°C. By substitution in equation (8.3) the rate of heat loss through the window per unit area is 106·2 W/m² (J/m² s).

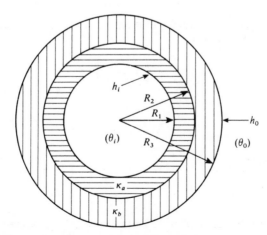

Figure 8.12 Heat conduction through wall of an
insulated pipe

Similarly, the rate of heat flow (q) through the walls of an insulated pipe, illustrated in Figure 8.12, is now given by:

$$\frac{q}{L} = \frac{2\pi(\theta_i - \theta_0)}{\dfrac{1}{h_i R_1} + \dfrac{\ln(R_2/R_1)}{\kappa_a} + \dfrac{\ln(R_3/R_2)}{\kappa_b} + \dfrac{1}{h_0 R_3}} \tag{8.4}$$

In this case we can consider the example of heat loss from an uninsulated polypropylene pipe having external and internal diameters of 75 mm and 67·5 mm, respectively (hence a wall thickness of 3·75 mm) carrying water at a controlled temperature of 60°C in a cold environment at 5°C. The thermal conductivity of polypropylene is about 0·21 W/m°C, h_i is 1700 W/m²°C and h_0 is 10 W/m²°C. The rate of heat loss per unit length of pipe is, by substitution in equation (8.4), 188 W/m.

8.4.1   Thermal Diffusivity and Heat Transfer

Consideration of thermal conductivity in section 8.4 referred to measurements of a system at equilibrium. In practical situations engineers are concerned frequently about non-equilibrium conditions as a component is heated or cooled, the heat both being conducted through the material and changing its temperature. Therefore, both thermal conductivity and enthalpy factors are involved and thermal diffusivity (α) is defined as the ratio of thermal conductivity (κ) to the heat capacity for unit volume

$$\alpha = \frac{\kappa}{\rho H}$$

where H is the heat capacity for unit mass (specific heat), and ρ is the density. If κ is expressed in W/m°C

$$\left(\frac{Jm}{m^2 \, s°C}\right)$$

H is expressed in

$$\frac{J}{kg°C}$$

ρ is expressed in

$$\frac{kg}{m^3}$$

then α is derived in units of m²/s. Data are usually presented as in Table 8.2, assuming that α is independent of temperature, which is a limitation on their use.

Table 8.2. Thermal Diffusivity Data

Polymer	Temperature range (°C)	'Mean' thermal diffusivity (m²/s)
LD polyethylene	20–190	0.9×10^{-7}
	20–270	1.0×10^{-7}
Polypropylene	20–230	0.9×10^{-7}
Poly (4-methylpentene-1)	20–260	1.0×10^{-7}
Polymethyl methacrylate	20–100	1.0×10^{-7}
	100–200	0.7×10^{-7}
Polycarbonate	20–270	1.1×10^{-7}
Polysulphone	20–270	1.1×10^{-7}
Polyethersulphone	20–160	1.25×10^{-7}
Polyvinyl chloride	20–60	1.1×10^{-7}
(unplasticized)	70–160	0.8×10^{-7}
Nylon 66	20–285	1.3×10^{-7}
Polytetrafluoroethylene	20–180	1.25×10^{-7}
Acetal copolymer	20–220	1.0×10^{-7}

There are many ways of applying thermal diffusivity data to the solution of heat transfer problems and the reader is referred to standard texts.[10–12] Briefly, charts or tables of relevant functions may be employed or numerical methods used, the last of these assuming importance in the last decade with the increasing availability of digital computers. However, the use of charts has much to recommend it for the approximate solution of problems commonly encountered in plastics engineering design as, for example, when a body of uniform temperature is subjected to a sudden change in temperature at its surface.

Fourier's equation for heat flow in one dimension is

$$\frac{\partial^2 \theta}{\partial x^2} = \frac{1}{\alpha} \frac{\partial \theta}{\partial t} \tag{8.5}$$

For non-steady-state conditions, solutions to this equation are in the form of infinite series, but following Gurney and Lurie,[13] Schack[14] and, later, Hands,[15] the information can be presented graphically for infinite slabs of finite thickness, for cylinders of infinite length and finite radius and for spheres. (Alternatively, tabulated data for analogous functions are available in Olson and Schultz's paper.[16]) In these treatments, dimensionless variables and parameters are defined as:

Relative time

$$\tau = \frac{t\alpha}{R^2}$$

where t is elapsed time; α is thermal diffusivity; R is radius of cylinder or sphere, or $\frac{1}{2}$ thickness of slab.

Unaccomplished temperature change

$$\Delta = \frac{\theta_i - \theta}{\theta_i - \theta_0}$$

where θ is temperature at time t; θ_0 is initial uniform temperature; θ_i is imposed temperature.

In plotting Δ against τ, curves are obtained which are functions also of two further dimensionless quantities r and m which are defined by:

$$r = \frac{a}{R}$$

where a is the distance from centre, axis, or mid-plane; (R is defined above).

$$m = \frac{\kappa}{hR}$$

where κ is thermal conductivity; h is thermal surface conductivity or surface heat transfer coefficient, defined as the quantity of heat flowing in unit time normal to the surface across unit area of the interface.

Solutions to the Fourier equation are given as curves of Δ against τ (Δ on log scale) parameters m and r (Gurney and Lurie), Δ against $1/m$ ($1/m$ on variable scale) parameter τ, $r = 0$ or 1 (Schack) and Δ against r, parameter τ, selected values of m (Hands), enabling heat transfer calculations to be made for the cases given above. For plastics which are of low thermal diffusivity, the last two forms of presentation are preferred for ease of interpretation unless very long timescales are involved.

If the samples cannot be regarded as infinite in at least some of their dimensions and are, therefore, outside the scope of the methods outlined above (say shortest dimension $> \frac{1}{4}$ longest dimension), solutions to heat transfer problems can still be obtained by Newman's method. For such a finite sample, heat transfer is considered with respect to each opposing pair of faces in turn, on the assumption that the remaining dimensions are infinite. In this way three values of the unaccomplished temperature change are obtained Δ_x, Δ_y and Δ_z and the final solution is the product

$$\Delta = \Delta_x \cdot \Delta_y \cdot \Delta_z.$$

This method is only applicable to right cylinders and rectangular parallelopipeds (bricks). In certain other cases, e.g. ellipsoids, approximations can be made but the heat transfer behaviour of irregularly shaped bodies is not amenable to easy calculation.

With many thermal data still presented in other than SI units the dimensionless variables approach has the added attraction that, provided numerators and denominators of the various ratios are in similar terms, the dimensionless parameters are independent of the units employed.

An illustrative example of the use of this approach is in the analysis of the cooling of extruded lace in a water bath. Consider the case of the extrusion of an acetal copolymer lace of radius R 1·6 mm. The initial temperature of the polymer is 190°C and it is extruded into a water bath at a temperature of 20°C. We wish to know the length of cooling bath required to solidify the polymer completely at a given linear haul-off rate. The thermal diffusivity (α) of the polymer is taken as 1×10^{-7} m²/s and its conductivity (κ) is 0·23 W/m°C. From differential scanning calorimetry cooling curves it is seen that this polymer supercools so that its peak freezing rate occurs at about 143°C. The time t taken to lower the centre line of the polymer to 140°C will be calculated. From the information given, values of the unaccomplished temperature Δ and also a value of m can be calculated.

$$\Delta = 0.71$$

and

$$m = \frac{\kappa}{Rh} = 0.09$$

where h is the heat transfer coefficient to water and is taken as being equal to 1700 W/m²°C.

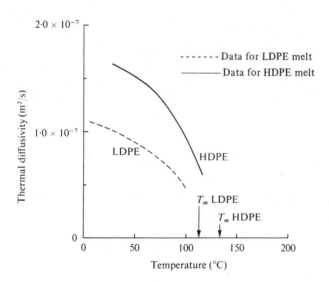

Figure 8.13 Thermal diffusivity vs. temperature: LDPE— density 920 kg/m³ (20°C), HDPE—density 959 kg/m³ (20°C).

Reading from the standard charts, e.g. those due to Hands,[15] we find

$$\tau = 0.16 = \frac{\alpha t}{R^2}$$

$$\therefore t = 4.1 \text{ s}$$

Therefore the length of bath required to solidify the polymer at a haul-off rate V m/s is $V.t = V.(4.1)$ metres, e.g. at a haul-off rate of 0·5 m/s bath length is $4.1 \times 0.5 = 2$ m. approximately.

This type of analysis is an approximation in that the thermal diffusivity of the polymer is assumed constant over the temperature range considered. In fact, the thermal diffusivity of polymers, especially the semi-crystalline polymers, varies quite markedly with temperature, as shown in the data for polyethylene in Figure 8.13. For a more accurate analysis these data would be used in a numerical approach requiring the use of a digital computer.

8.5   THERMODYNAMIC PROPERTIES

The fundamental thermodynamic properties of thermoplastics—the rate of change of entropy with pressure at constant temperature $(\partial S/\partial P)_T$ and the rate of change of entropy with temperature at constant volume $(\partial S/\partial T)_V$— derive from measurements of specific heat, specific volume and temperature. When a large pressure drop results from the rapid flow of a thermoplastic melt through a channel, e.g. in the sprues and runners of an injection moulding machine, the exact calculation of material flow depends on the temperature decrease during adiabatic bulk expansion $(\partial T/\partial P)_S$. The measured rate of change of temperature with pressure at constant entropy agrees closely with that calculated as

$$\left(\frac{\partial T}{\partial P}\right)_S = - \left(\frac{\partial S}{\partial P}\right)_T \left(\frac{\partial S}{\partial T}\right)_P^{-1}$$

Similarly, the rate of change of pressure with temperature at constant volume $(\delta P/\partial T)_V$ may be calculated from

$$\left(\frac{\partial P}{\partial T}\right)_V = \frac{K}{V} \left(\frac{\partial S}{\partial P}\right)_T$$

where K is the bulk modulus and V the specific volume. Values of the derived thermodynamic properties $(\partial T/\partial P)_S$ and $(\partial T/\partial P)_V$ for a range of thermoplastics are presented in Table 8.3.[17]

Table 8.3. Some Thermodynamic Properties of Thermoplastics

Material	$\left(\dfrac{\partial T}{\partial P}\right)_S$ °C/Nm^{-2}	$\left(\dfrac{\partial T}{\partial P}\right)_V$ °C/Nm^{-2}
PVC	$1 \cdot 1 \times 10^{-7}$	$16 \cdot 0 \times 10^{-7}$
Nylon 66	$1 \cdot 2 \times 10^{-7}$	$11 \cdot 0 \times 10^{-7}$
Poly(methyl methacrylate)	$1 \cdot 2 \times 10^{-7}$	$13 \cdot 0 \times 10^{-7}$
Polystyrene	$1 \cdot 5 \times 10^{-7}$	$13 \cdot 0 \times 10^{-7}$
Polyethylene (high-density)	$1 \cdot 5 \times 10^{-7}$	$13 \cdot 0 \times 10^{-7}$
Acetal copolymer	$1 \cdot 4 \times 10^{-7}$	$14 \cdot 0 \times 10^{-7}$
Polyethylene (low-density)	$1 \cdot 6 \times 10^{-7}$	$16 \cdot 0 \times 10^{-7}$
Polypropylene	$2 \cdot 2 \times 10^{-7}$	$19 \cdot 0 \times 10^{-7}$

8.6 THERMAL EXPANSION

When materials are heated they generally expand, the expansion depending on the temperature attained. Expansion occurs in linear and area dimensions and in volume, the linear and area expansions being affected by any anisotropy in the sample. In such circumstances it is usual to measure thermal expansion in the direction or plane of maximum orientation and perpendicularly to this.

The relationship between thermal expansion and temperature is best given graphically although values of the coefficient of (linear) (area) (volume)

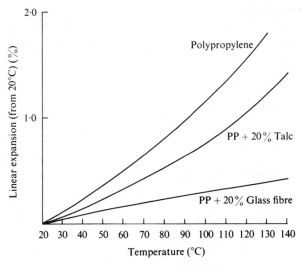

Figure 8.14 Linear thermal expansion vs. temperature: polypropylene and filled grades

expansion are sometimes quoted. Such coefficients are the slopes of the corresponding expansion vs. temperature curves. Measurements are usually referred to a base at 20°C unless otherwise specified.

Figure 8.14 shows data for polypropylene. Data are usually given for dry plastics, the effect of absorbed water on the dimensions being assumed to be additive (see Chapter 9).

The thermal expansion of plastics is high compared with that of metals but is reduced by fillers. Typical comparative data are given in Table 8.4.

Table 8.4

Material	Coefficient of linear expansion at 20°C $\mu m/m°C$
Mild steel	11
Brass	19
Acetal copolymer	80
Polypropylene	110
Low-density polyethylene	200–220
Nylon 6:6	90
Nylon 6:6 + 30% glass fibre	30–70 (dependent on orientation)

As with thermal conductivity, thermal expansion is affected by crystallinity in any one class of material: the higher the crystallinity the lower the thermal expansion, although as a class crystalline plastics have higher thermal expansions than the glassy amorphous ones. This is because the rubbery amorphous regions of crystalline plastics are more temperature sensitive than the glassy amorphous plastics, as shown in Table 8.5.

Table 8.5

Classification	Material	Coefficient of linear expansion at 20°C $\mu m/m°C$
Amorphous or glassy	Poly(vinyl chloride)	80
	Polystyrene	60–80
	Polycarbonate	70
	Poly(methyl methacrylate)	70
Crystalline	Polypropylene	110
	High-density polyethylene	110–130
	Low-density polyethylene	200–220
	Nylon 66	90
Rubbery	Natural rubber	220

The measurement of thermal expansion of plastics presents no problems: equipment of only moderate sensitivity is adequate in view of the high thermal expansions involved. Experimental technique is dominated by the low thermal conductivity of plastics, thus requiring relatively long timescales for the system to attain thermal equilibrium.

8.7 REFERENCES

1. BS 2782, Method 102 G, H (British Standards Institution), *Temperature of Deflection under Load at* 1·81, 0·45 *MN/m²*.
2. ASTM D-648-56 (American Society for Testing and Materials), *Test for Deflection Temperature of Plastics under Load.*
3. ASTM D-746-70 (American Society for Testing and Materials), *Method of Test for Brittleness Temperature of Plastics and Elastomers by Impact.*
4. M. E. Spaght, S. B. Thomas and G. S. Parks, 'Some heat-capacity data on organic compounds obtained with a radiation calorimeter', *J. Phys. Chem.*, **36**, 882 (1932).
5. BS 2782 Method 102D (British Standards Institution), *Vicat Softening Point.*
6. A. Turner-Jones, unpublished data.
7. H. Wilski, 'Specific heat of polypropylene', *Kunststoffe*, **50**, 335 (1960).
8. K. Deutsch, E. A. W. Hoff and W. Reddish, 'Relation between the structure of polymers and their dynamic mechanical and electrical properties', *J. Poly. Sci.*, **13**, 565 (1954).
9. A. Turner-Jones, unpublished data.
10. H. S. Carslaw and J. C. Jaeger, *Conduction of Heat in Solids*, 2nd Edition, Oxford University Press, 1959.
11. M. Jakob, *Heat Transfer*, Vols. I and II, Wiley, 1949, 1957.
12. W. H. McAdams, *Heat Transmission*, 3rd Edition, McGraw-Hill, 1954.
13. H. P. Gurney and J. Lurie, 'Charts for estimating temperature distribution in heating or cooling solid shapes', *Ind. Eng. Chem.*, **15**, 1170 (1923).
14. A. Schack, *Stahl u Eisen*, **50**, 1289 (1930).
15. D. Hands, 'Simple methods for heat flow calculations', *RAPRA Technical Review No. 60*, Rubber and Plastics Research Association, Shawbury (1971).
16. F. C. W. Olson and O. T. Schultz, 'Temperatures in solids during heating or cooling', and 'Tables for the numerical solution of the heating equation', *Ind. Eng. Chem.*, **34**, 874 (1942).
17. F. N. Cogswell, 'The influence of pressure on the viscosity of polymer melts', *Plastics and Polymers*, **41**, No. 151, 39 (1973).

8.8 FURTHER READING

BS 4618, *Recommendations for the Presentation of Plastics Design Data* (British Standards Institution) Part 3.1: 'Linear Thermal Expansion'. Part 3.2: 'Heat Content'. Part 3.3: 'Thermal Conductivity'.

BS 874 (1965) (British Standards Institution) *Methods of Determining Thermal Properties.*

B. Ke (Ed.), 'Newer methods of polymer characterization', *Polymer Review*, Vol. 6, Interscience, 1964.

P. E. Slade and L. T. Jenkins (Eds.), *Techniques and Methods of Polymer Evaluation*, Vol. 1, 'Thermal analysis', Arnold (London), Dekker (New York), 1966; Vol. 2, 'Thermal evaluation techniques', Dekker (New York), 1970.

9

Miscellaneous Physical Properties

by G. Ross and A. W. Birley

9.1 OPTICAL PROPERTIES

The optical behaviour of plastics is relevant to a wide variety of situations ranging from technically trivial requirements in packaging to critical conditions in optical instruments. Lighting and display are two other areas in which optical properties are relevant at the design stage. The success of

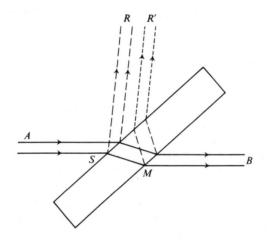

Figure 9.1 Light incident on a slab of non-opaque material

plastics in these applications depends on the rational exploitation of one or several property areas. These areas are most usefully treated by considering a parallel beam of light as incident on a surface of a plastics slab (see Figure 9.1). The light may be affected in the following ways.

(1) Some may be reflected geometrically along path SR.

(2) Depending on the nature (topography) of the surface, some of the incident radiation may be scattered by the surface of the sample.

(3) A portion of the light will be refracted in the sample, its path depending on the average refractive index, and emerge at M.

(4) A portion of the light incident on the sample at S may be absorbed by the sample along the path SM. Excluding plastics deliberately coloured, the absorption occurring in the visible range is, in general, very low.

(5) A further quantity of the light traversing the sample SM may be scattered by optical inhomogeneities (local variations in refractive index) within the sample. Scattering may be forwards or backwards, defined by a scattering angle of 0–90° and 90–180° respectively as measured from the direction of the incident beam.

(6) A proportion of the light traversing the sample will be reflected geometrically at M, eventually emerging substantially at R'. A certain amount of the light arriving at M will be scattered by the roughness of the exit surface.

(7) The remainder of the light reaching M emerges in a direction MB parallel to the incident beam (if the slab has parallel faces).

Internal reflection may continue the processes (1)–(7), but its effect is negligible.

It is convenient to divide consideration of these phenomena into four sections, each relevant in a particular area of application for plastics.

9.1.1   Refraction

Refraction is concerned, as the term implies, with the 'bending' of light as it passes from one medium to another. It is extremely important in lens design, and is caused by a change in velocity of light as it passes from one medium to another and the refractive index of a material is defined for a specified wavelength in vacuum (or a specific frequency) as the ratio of the velocity of light in vacuum to the velocity in the material. As the velocity of radiation in vacuum differs by less than 0·1 % from that in air, refractive indices are frequently quoted against air as the standard. The refractive index, n, is measured as the ratio of the sin of the angle of incidence, i, to the sin of the angle of refraction, r_t, (Figure 9.2).

$$n = \frac{\sin i}{\sin r_t}$$

The variation of refractive index with the wavelength of light in vacuum is given by the dispersion curve (Figure 9.3). The spectral lines and their wavelengths in vacuum for which the refractive index n_x is usually measured are given in Table 9.1, although presentation of the data in the form of a dispersion curve is preferred. Values of refractive index are assumed to be at 20°C unless otherwise stated.

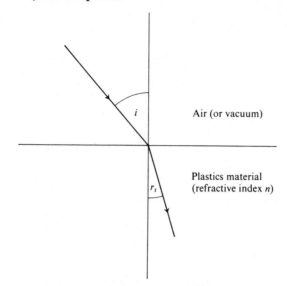

Figure 9.2 Refraction of light

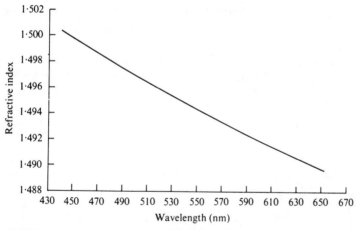

Figure 9.3 Optical dispersion curve: acrylic cast sheet (Perspex) dry, 20°C

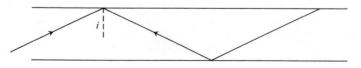

Figure 9.4 Principle of a light pipe

Table 9.1

Refractive index subscript x	Wavelength nm	Source
	780·0	Rb
A′	768·0	K[a]
C	656·3	H
C′	643·8	Cd
D	589·3	Na[a]
d	587·6	He
e	546·1	Hg
F	486·1	H
F′	480·0	Cd
g	435·8	Hg
h	404·7	Hg

[a] Mean of the doublet.

An important application of transparent plastics is light pipes and fibre optics, which are gaining increasing markets because of their comparative lack of brittleness and easy manufacture. Light in the pipe is totally internally reflected if its angle of incidence is greater than $\sin^{-1} 1/n$. For example, for 'Perspex' acrylic pipe at 20°C, dry, the value of this angle is 42° for the line e of mercury.

The variation of refractive index (usually n_d) with temperature is best described by a curve of refractive index vs. temperature (Figure 9.5). The

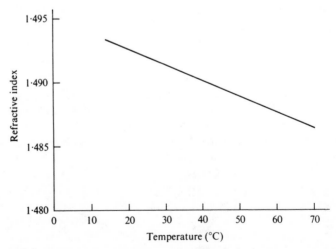

Figure 9.5   Refractive index vs. temperature: acrylic cast sheet (Perspex) dry, 589·3 nm

temperature coefficient of refractive index at 20°C, $\Delta n_d / \Delta T$, is sometimes used to express the temperature dependence.

Birefringence Δn is the result of structural anisotropy and is defined as the maximum algebraic difference between two refractive indices measured in two directions perpendicular to one another. It depends on the mean orientation of chain molecules in the plastics material since the molecular chains are usually themselves optically anisotropic. To exemplify, a sample of poly(ethylene terephthalate) which had been planar oriented by hot stretching in the plane gave the following results:

$$\gamma - \alpha = 189 \times 10^{-3}$$

$$\gamma - \beta = 30 \times 10^{-3} \quad \text{(Data at 20°C, 589·3 nm)}$$

where α, β and γ are refractive indices perpendicular to the plane of orientation (α) and in the plane of orientation (β, γ) β and γ being mutually at 90° and also being, respectively, the minimum and maximum refractive indices in the plane.

The relative stress optical coefficient defines the relationship between the birefringence induced in a material and the stress producing it

$$\Delta n = CP$$

where P is the stress and C the stress optical coefficient.

9.1.2   Transparency

Transparency is a general concept and depends on the material's optical homogeneity, both in the bulk and at the surfaces. Plastics, especially amorphous materials, are potentially transparent if they are homogeneous: examples are poly(methyl methacrylate) and polystyrene. Lack of optical homogeneity, i.e. variations in refractive index, leads to two effects: aberration of the image, frequently referred to as 'loss of clarity' and loss of contrast in the image by scattering of some of the radiation. These two effects are closely interconnected but distinct aspects of what is generally known as 'transparency'. Although a comprehensive theoretical treatment of scattering has not been worked out, for most purposes transparency can be described by certain characteristics which are discussed in the following paragraphs.

Let us consider a monochromatic parallel beam of unpolarized flux ϕ, falling perpendicularly on a (plastics) film or sheet immersed in a liquid of matching refractive index. A certain amount of flux, ϕ_{sc} will be scattered in all directions, a part ϕ_A will be absorbed by the material and the remainder, ϕ_{undev} will be transmitted without deviation (see Figure 9.6).

$$\phi_{undev} = \phi - \phi_A - \phi_{sc}$$

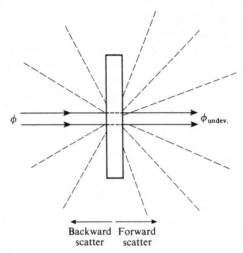

Backward Forward
scatter   scatter

Figure 9.6 Transmission of light through a
plastics sheet

In the above expression inelastic effects such as fluorescence or Raman scattering are neglected. The direct transmission factor or specular transmittance T is defined by the ratio

$$T = \frac{\phi_{\text{undev}}}{\phi}$$

T is a function of the wavelength of the light, which should be stated, and of the thickness of the sample. If the sample is not immersed reflective losses at the incident and emergent surfaces must be taken into account.

For materials of high transparency (i.e. weak scatterers), the connection between the specular transmittance and the thickness of sample traversed, l, can be given approximately by

$$T = e^{-(\sigma+K)l}$$

where σ is a measure of the amount of light scattering and is frequently known as the *turbidity* (or scattering coefficient); K measures the amount of light absorbed and is known as the *absorption coefficient*. The sum of $\sigma + K$ is usually measured practically and is the *attenuation coefficient* or *extinction coefficient*. For most plastics materials K is small compared with σ and for all practical purposes the extinction coefficient is, to a good approximation, equal to the turbidity. Both K and σ have dimensions (length)$^{-1}$ and are usually measured in cm^{-1}. T is a dimensionless fraction, usually expressed as a percentage.

The scattered light may be visualized as the sum of that scattered forwards ϕ_{sc}^f plus that scattered backwards ϕ_{sc}^b

$$\phi_{sc} = \phi_{sc}^f + \phi_{sc}^b$$

where the indices f and b refer to scattering in the angles 0 to 90° and 90° to 180° respectively as measured from the direction of the incident beam.

The total flux transmitted ϕ_T is given by the relation:

$$\phi_T = \phi_{undev} + \phi_{sc}^f$$

and the forward scattered fraction χ_{sc}^f as

$$\chi_{sc}^f = \frac{\phi_{sc}^f}{\phi_T}$$

All these characteristics are functions of the wavelength.

The loss in contrast resulting from viewing an object through a scattering medium, the light source being on the same side as the object, is due to the light scattered forward in general at high angles. It is conveniently expressed as the forward scattered fraction χ_{sc}^f and is often termed *haze*. It is sometimes possible to characterize haze as the proportion of light scattered between two specified arbitrary angles, compared with the total transmitted light, ϕ_T. In the ASTM and BS tests, the scattered light is measured between $2\frac{1}{2}°$ and 90°, which are set angles in the instrument normally employed. The quantity thus determined, also frequently known as 'haze', differs from the forward scattered fraction χ_{sc}^f by the light scattered in the region $0°-2\frac{1}{2}°$: for some materials this may be substantial and lead to a lack of correlation between the standard measurement and visual effects. It is important to distinguish between surface scattering and bulk effects; the former is minimized by 'oiling out' the surface with a liquid of refractive index similar to that of the plastics sample leaving only the contribution due to bulk scattering. The 'milkiness' of translucent samples viewed from the side on which light is incident is due to back-scattering.

Clarity is a measure of the capacity of the sample to permit details in the object to be resolved in the image. Clarity is perfect only when no light is scattered by the sample; it is strongly dependent on the angular distribution of the scattered intensity and on the distance between the object viewed and the sample. In the usual method of assessment, the change in angular separation of points on the object which can just be resolved when a sheet of the plastics material is interposed between the object and the eye is used as a measure of clarity.

Figure 9.7 illustrates the loss of contrast due to haze: comparison of the outer region with the inner circle illustrates the loss of contrast in the former due to haze. The central section is an 'oiled' surface under a circular microscope

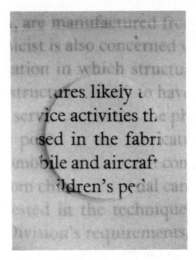

Figure 9.7   Haze: compare the oiled-
out centre circle with the remainder.
The loss of contrast is due to surface
scattering

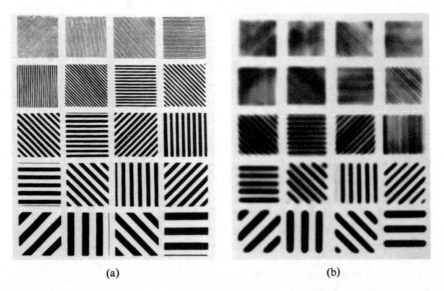

(a)   (b)

Figure 9.8   Clarity charts: (a) without and (b) with, a plastic film placed between
chart and observer

cover glass showing that the scattering originated at the surface of the material. Figure 9.8 illustrates the loss in resolution observed when a sheet of poor clarity is interposed between the standard charts and the observer. Note that there is very little loss in contrast in this case and very little loss in resolution in Figure 9.7.

9.1.3 Reflective Properties

When a beam of light meets a medium of different refractive index, a certain proportion of the light is reflected according to the laws of optics, i.e. the angle of incidence i is equal to the angle of reflection r (Figure 9.9). Reflection

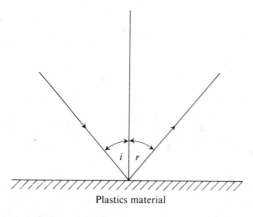

Plastics material

Figure 9.9 Geometric reflection of light at a plane surface

occurs at any change of refractive index: in other words, light passing through a sheet or film specimen suffers reflective losses at both the air–plastics and the plastics–air interfaces. For normal incidence, the proportion of light reflected at each surface, assumed perfectly smooth and flat, is given by

$$\frac{(n_A - n_B)^2}{(n_A + n_B)^2}$$

where n_A and n_B are the refractive indices of the two media, but in the general case the amount of light reflected depends strongly on the angle of incidence. The direct reflection factor R is defined by the ratio of light flux reflected according to the laws of optics ϕ_R and the incident light flux ϕ (assumed to be unpolarized).

$$R = \frac{\phi_R}{\phi}$$

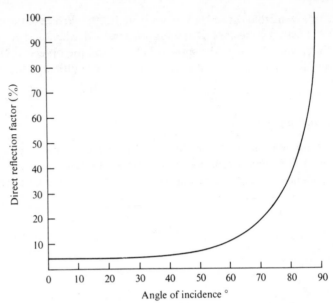

Figure 9.10   Direct reflection factor vs. angle of incidence 20°C, 589·3 nm. Air-acrylic cast sheet interface (Perspex) dry

The information is best presented as a curve of direct reflection factor against angle of incidence, as illustrated in Figure 9.10.

The general appearance of a surface can be assessed by comparing the flux scattered within a certain solid angle, ωr, around the geometrical reflection direction ϕ_r with the incident flux ϕ (Figure 9.11). The gloss, G, characterizing the appearance of the surface, is defined by

$$G = \frac{\phi_{\omega r}}{\phi}$$

This ratio should be given for various angles of incidence and for various solid angles about the geometrical reflection direction. Commercially available instruments are usually restricted to determinations at only one solid angle but, nevertheless, they provide a useful, if arbitrary, measurement.

The *total reflection factor* R_T is defined, for normal incidence, as the ratio between the total backwards scattered light energy (including geometric reflection) and the incident radiation energy,

$$R_T = \frac{\phi_{sc}^b}{\phi}$$

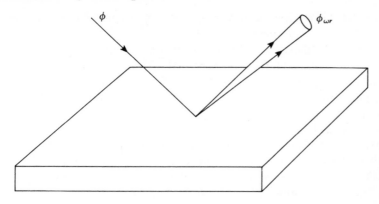

Figure 9.11 Measurement of surface gloss

9.1.4 Light Transfer

The *total transmission factor* (*total transmittance*) is defined by the ratio of the total transmitted light ϕ_T to the incident radiation assumed concentrated in a parallel beam normal to the surface.

$$\text{Total transmission factor} = \frac{\phi_T}{\phi}$$

It depends on the thickness of the sample and the wavelength distribution of the illuminant and is of considerable importance in the design of lighting diffusers.

A further effect, the selective or non-selective absorption of the light, may occur, resulting in the development of colour or greyness (blackness), respectively. This indeed is the basis of dyeing or colouring of materials but discussion of this topic is outside the scope of this book.

9.2 FRICTION

When two bodies are in contact and one of them moves or tends to move in relation to the other, a force develops opposing the movement in a direction tangential to the surfaces in contact. If the two surfaces are initially at rest, static friction is involved, whilst the force developed if the two surfaces are in relative motion is kinetic (or dynamic) friction. It is further necessary to distinguish between sliding friction, as of a sledge, and rolling friction, as of a wheel. Overcoming friction can lead to a waste of useful power in a mechanical system but a major problem is the damage caused by wear: further, in extreme cases the heat generated can cause seizing of the surfaces. This last phenomenon can be utilized in the frictional welding of plastics where sufficient local heat is generated to melt and weld the surfaces.

The two fundamental laws of friction which apply in the absence of lubricants state that the frictional force is proportional to the load and is independent of the area of contact of the surfaces. They lead to a definition of the coefficient of friction μ, the ratio of the tangential to the normal force between the two surfaces.

The coefficient of friction is not a material constant: it depends on the nature and type of finish of the two surfaces in contact and is affected also by the load, the rate of relative movement of the two surfaces, environmental conditions (temperature and humidity) and the presence of liquids or dusts which may act as lubricants or abrasives. The effect of temperature is most marked with less rigid plastics where some correlation of friction coefficient with mechanical hysteresis has been observed. Thus, care must be exercised in interpreting friction data that the operating conditions of the test are similar to those pertaining in the application under consideration.

Quite simple equipment can be used to measure the frictional force, although the number of variables affecting the measurement virtually prohibit complete coverage. In addition to factors given above, many geometries of the surfaces in contact are possible including plate–plate, pin and plate, crossed cylinders and rotating shaft systems. For reproducible results, great care must be taken in the preparation of the sample surface. Even the smoothest surfaces have projecting asperities about 10 nm (0·4 micro inches) high. When two surfaces appear to touch, true contact is achieved only over a fraction of the nominal areas of contact: this fraction is commonly about 0·01 % but can be as large as 1 %.

When sliding occurs between two surfaces, the frictional force is made up of two parts. The first is a result of adhesion (or cohesion) at the points of true contact where strong junctions are formed by plastic flow, and the shearing of these junctions is the main cause of frictional resistance. The second arises when the asperities of the harder material plough through the surface of the softer material. A simple outline theory of the first effect can explain the basic laws of friction for materials which deform plastically under the high local pressures.

$$\text{True area of contact, } A = \frac{\text{Load, } W}{\text{mean yield stress of asperities, } Y}$$

$$\text{Friction force, } F = AS = \frac{WS}{Y}$$

where S is the mean shear strength of asperities. Hence

$$\text{Coefficient of friction, } \mu = \frac{F}{W} = \frac{S}{Y}$$

The same approximate treatment can be applied to brittle solids and to plastics. Such differences as exist between the friction of metals and polymers arise from the differences between the plastic response of metals and the viscoelastic response of plastics. Thus, as load is reduced, plastics deform in an increasingly viscoelastic manner and the coefficient of friction increases steadily. Time-dependent effects have been observed with plastics particularly if wear debris collects and there is a more marked sensitivity to temperature because plastics are working relatively near to their softening points. The softness of plastics often allows a transfer of material to the mating surface: in such cases the coefficient of friction tends towards the value for plastic on plastic even when the surface in contact with the plastic is metal. Typical values of the coefficient of friction for surfaces at least one of which is a plastics material are 0·3 to 0·6 but polytetrafluoroethylene is an exceptional material giving values of 0·05 to 0·1 against most other surfaces. A possible explanation is that the structure of PTFE leads to low interchain forces and a low value of S, the mean shear strength. On the other hand, the molecular chains are rigid, giving a fairly high value of Y, the mean yield stress. Further, because of likely transfer of PTFE to the mating surface and the high orientation induced in this material, a further increase in the mean yield stress is to be expected. The combination of these factors leads to an abnormally low value for the coefficient of friction.

This combination of rigidity and small area of contact with low shear strength can also be achieved in two-component systems. Thus plastics are often reinforced with fillers to reduce friction and wear: in bearings it is common practice to use a thin surface layer of a soft alloy or plastics material on a rigid steel backing, giving systems with abnormally low co-efficients of friction which increase with increasing speed, preventing stick–slip phenomena.

One of the most important applications of the frictional properties of plastics is in journal bearings where the use of plastics avoids the catastrophic failure characteristics of metal bearings which, in the absence of lubrication, will seize and cause considerable damage to the shaft. Plastics behave well in highly abrasive conditions, where their softness enables them to absorb abrasive particles and thus avoid further damage. Plastics components also have the advantage of quietness in operation and good impact resistance. The main disadvantages are poor dimensional stability, low thermal conductivity and low strength. All these disadvantages are largely overcome by the use of plastics as thin surface films, supported by a strong metal backing.

In designing conventional metallic bearings engineers often use the PV factor, the product of the pressure P (defined as the total load divided by the nominal projected area of the bearing) and the relative velocity of the bearing surfaces, V. Thus PV has the dimensions of a rate of energy dissipation; indeed, there is a direct proportionality if the coefficient of friction is constant.

Approximately, it is possible to quote a maximum permissible PV value beyond which a given bearing will fail, a concept which can also be applied to plastics bearings. By calculating the PV rating for a given application, it can be decided whether such a use is feasible and whether to proceed with prototypes, provided the limiting PV data are available for the materials under consideration. In practice the PV limit is dependent on velocity and temperature and critically dependent on the degree of lubrication.

The choice of a plastics material for a given bearing application depends primarily on the amount of lubrication to be provided: PTFE with various fillers is excellent for dry bearings. When hydrodynamic lubrication is provided, the surfaces are separated by a comparatively thick layer of lubricant: the frictional properties are unimportant and a plastic will be chosen, if at all, for softness, low wear, compatibility and cost. The intermediate case is that of boundary lubrication where the surfaces are separated by a layer of lubricant a few molecules thick. Nylon and acetal polymers are commonly used in light-duty applications because of their ability to work well with only initial

Table 9.2. Coefficients of Friction

Specimen		Sliding speed (mm/s)					
Slider	Plate	0·03	0·1	0·4	0·8	3·0	10·6
(a) Unlubricated tests							
PP (as moulded)	PP (as moulded)	0·54	0·65	0·71	0·77	0·77	0·71
Nylon (as moulded)	Nylon (as moulded)	0·63	—	0·69	0·70	0·70	0·65
PP (abraded)	PP (abraded)	0·26	0·29	0·22	0·21	0·31	0·27
Nylon (machined)	Nylon (machined)	0·42	—	0·44	0·46	0·46	0·47
Mild Steel	PP (abraded)	0·24	0·26	0·27	0·29	0·30	0·31
Mild Steel	Nylon (machined)	0·33	—	0·33	0·33	0·30	0·30
PP (abraded)	Mild Steel	0·33	0·34	0·37	0·37	0·38	0·38
Nylon (machined)	Mild Steel	0·39	—	0·41	0·41	0·40	0·40
(b) Water lubricated tests							
PP (abraded)	PP (abraded)	0·25	0·26	0·29	0·30	0·28	0·31
Nylon (machined)	Nylon (machined)	0·27	—	0·24	0·22	0·21	0·19
Mild Steel	PP (abraded)	0·23	0·25	0·26	0·26	0·26	0·22
Mild Steel	Nylon (machined)	0·23	—	0·20	0·20	0·19	0·17
PP (abraded)	Mild Steel	0·25	0·25	0·26	0·26	0·25	0·25
Nylon (machined)	Mild Steel	0·20	—	0·23	0·23	0·22	0·18
(c) Liquid paraffin lubricated tests							
PP (abraded)	PP (abraded)	0·29	0·26	0·24	0·25	0·22	0·21
Nylon (machined)	Nylon (machined)	0·22	—	0·15	0·13	0·11	0·08
Mild Steel	PP (abraded)	0·17	0·17	0·16	0·16	0·14	0·14
Mild Steel	Nylon (machined)	0·16	—	0·11	0·09	0·08	0·08
PP (abraded)	Mild Steel	0·31	0·30	0·30	0·29	0·27	0·25
Nylon (machined)	Mild Steel	0·26	—	0·15	0·12	0·07	0·04

or infrequent lubrication. In such applications, molybdenum-disulphide-filled nylon is often preferred because of better lubrication, lower friction and better abrasion resistance.

The improvement obtained by lubrication of plastics is less well marked than with metals. However, heavier loadings can often be used and the *PV* limit may be increased by as much as a factor of ten. With nylon bearings, slight initial lubrication has a most marked effect and in these circumstances nylon can easily out-perform metal. Water can be used to lubricate plastics in such applications as pumps. The extreme pressure lubricants, which rely for their functioning on chemical reaction with the metal, are of no use with plastics. Occasionally, friction and wear are increased by lubrication: in such cases it seems likely that the plastic material is swollen and softened by the lubricant. This can be avoided by care in the selection of the lubricant. Some illustrative results are given in Table 9.2, obtained at 20°C between a loaded hemisphere (slider) and a flat surface (plate) at a load of 2 Kg.

9.3 WEAR

Wear is usually considered under four main headings.

(1) Adhesive wear.
(2) Abrasive wear.
(3) Corrosive wear.
(4) Surface fatigue.

Adhesive wear is a natural consequence of the shearing of the actual junctions between surfaces and is always present when surfaces in contact move relative to one another. By using plastics rather than metals, adhesive forces and, therefore, adhesive wear are reduced and the disastrous effects of seizure can be avoided completely. Abrasive wear is caused by abrasive particles which may be introduced from outside or may be part of the wear debris. The softness of plastics is an advantage here because such particles may sink below the surface and not be accessible for further wear. Corrosive wear resulting from interaction of corrosion and mechanical forces is not a serious problem with plastics. On the other hand, surface fatigue is important, particularly in such applications as gear teeth.

There is not a direct relationship between friction and wear although factors which lead to an increase in friction will usually cause increased wear. Performance in a standard test for 'abrasion resistance' is of little design value for predicting wear and satisfactory predictions of wear resistance can only be made after long-term testing in a rig which approximates to the working conditions.

9.4 FURTHER READING

BS 4618, *Recommendations for the Presentation of Plastics Design Data*, Part 5.3, 'Optical properties', British Standards Institution, 1972.

ISO R489, *Determination of the Refractive Index of Transparent Plastics*, International Standards Organization.

ASTM D542-50, *Test for Index of Refraction of Transparent Organic Plastics*, American Society for Testing and Materials, 1970.

ASTM D1746-70, *Test for Transparency of Plastics Sheeting*, American Society for Testing and Materials, 1972.

ASTM D1003-61, *Test for Haze and Luminous Transmittance of Transparent Plastics* American Society for Testing and Materials, 1970.

BS 2782, *Methods of Testing Plastics*, Part 515A, 'Haze of film', British Standards Institution.

ASTM D523-67, *Test for Specular Gloss*, American Society for Testing and Materials.

ASTM D2457-70, *Test for Specular Gloss of Plastic Films*, American Society for Testing and Materials, 1972.

BS 2782, *Methods of Testing Plastics*, Part 515B 'Gloss (45°) of sheet', British Standards Institution.

F. P. Bowden and D. Tabor, *Friction and Lubrication of Solids*, Part 1, 1954, Part 2 (1969), Oxford.

F. P. Bowden and D. Tabor, 'Friction, lubrication and wear: a survey of work during the last decade', *Brit. J. Appl. Phys.*, **17**, 1521 (1966).

H. Hachmann and E. Strickk, 'Friction and wear of unlubricated systems of plastics paired with steel', *Kunststoffe*, **59**, 45 (1969).

C. O. L. Juulman, 'Haze and clarity of plastic sheeting', *Kunststoffe*, **61**, 843 (1971).

M. Kerker, *The Scattering of Light and other Electromagnetic Radiation*, Academic Press, 1969.

I. V. Kragelskii, *Friction and Wear* (translated by L. Ransom and J. K. Lancaster), Butterworth, 1965.

G. Ross *et al.*, 'An instrument for measuring the direct transmission factor of luminous flux in inhomogeneous media', *Optica Acta*, **18**, 839 (1971).

C. Ross and A. W. Birley, 'Optical properties of polymeric materials and their measurement', *J. Phys. D: Appl. Phys.* **6**, 795 (1973).

E. Schuch, 'Transparometer for translucent materials', *Kunststoffe*, **56**, 350 (1966).

H. Vetz and V. Hakenjos, 'Sliding friction and wear tests and plastics', *Kunststoffe*, **59**, 161 (1969).

10

Miscellaneous Chemical Properties

by A. W. Birley

10.1 INTRODUCTION

Plastics, in common with other engineering materials, are subject to constraints in use, resulting from interaction with the environment. With plastics, such interactions are sometimes reversible, e.g. absorption of liquid, or they may be irreversible, e.g. oxidation by exposure at elevated temperatures to air for prolonged times. In contradistinction, metal-environment interactions are almost always irreversible; corrosion and oxidation are perhaps the best examples. In the present treatment, distinction is made between plastics–environment interactions which are largely physical in nature and from which the plastics material can be recovered by simple physical processes (evaporation, vacuum treatment, etc.) and chemical interactions resulting in permanent change of the plastics material.

It has already been noted in Chapter 2 that few of the plastics offered commercially are pure polymers. Most contain additives such as plasticizers, heat stabilizers, antioxidants or pigments and some consist of blends of polymers. The chemical resistance of any material will depend on the nature and amount of each of the ingredients and detailed information on the likely behaviour of a particular material in a given environment is best obtained from the raw materials manufacturer.

10.2 PLASTICS–LIQUIDS SYSTEMS: PHYSICAL INTERACTION

The molecular chains of thermoplastics are held together only by weak interchain (secondary) forces and not by chemical bonds inherent in cross-linked systems. Separation of the chains of a thermoplastics material, therefore, does not involve the breaking of primary chemical bonds and consequently the interaction between solvents and such plastics is not qualitatively different from solvent interactions with organic substances of lower molecular weight. Based on this analysis some broad generalizations can be made which give an indication of the probable usefulness of thermoplastics in a given situation and within their working temperature ranges.

(1) Plastics are generally resistant to weak acids, weak alkalis and salt solutions. Strong oxidizing acids may attack plastics chemically, causing discolouration and embrittlement.

(2) Fuels, fats, oils and organic solvents may interact with plastics causing swelling, softening and ultimate dissolution. The degree of resistance depends on the nature of the plastics material, the nature of the solvent, and the temperature: it can vary from complete to very poor. The rate at which the fluid penetrates a plastics material is governed by the diffusion coefficient: the approach to equilibrium absorption may be extremely slow, particularly at ordinary temperatures. Plastics give highly viscous solutions and the maximum solubility may be quite low. When considering plastics–liquids interactions, 'like dissolves like' is a useful if abbreviated rule. In somewhat more refined terms, non-polar plastics, such as the polyolefines, are most susceptible to attack by hydrocarbon solvents, although crystallinity in the plastics material is a hindrance to easy solution and high temperatures are necessary. At the other extreme, polar polymers, e.g. polyamides, are resistant to hydrocarbons but susceptible to highly polar solvents that are hydrogen bonding, e.g. phenol. Some examples are given in Table 10.1. The effect of liquid absorption on properties has been discussed in Chapter 6.

A particular case of interaction with liquids resulting in a change in physical properties with no apparent chemical attack is afforded by environmental stress cracking which has been discussed in Chapter 6.

10.3 PLASTICS–LIQUIDS SYSTEMS: CHEMICAL INTERACTION

Two of the most important classes of reaction are hydrolysis (or aqueous attack) and oxidation resulting from attack by oxidizing solutions, particularly concentrated oxidizing acids.

Hydrolysis is a particular problem with condensation polymers, that is polymers of which the chains have been formed by elimination of water or other small molecules from reactive end groups: thus, for example

$$-OH \ + \ HO-\overset{\overset{\displaystyle O}{\|}}{C}- \quad \longrightarrow \quad -O-\overset{\overset{\displaystyle O}{\|}}{C}- \ + \ H_2O \qquad \text{(polyester)}$$

or

$$-NH_2 + HO\overset{\overset{\displaystyle O}{\|}}{C}- \quad \longrightarrow \quad -NH-\overset{\overset{\displaystyle O}{\|}}{C}- \ + \ H_2O \qquad \text{(polyamide)}$$

or

$$-\overset{\overset{\displaystyle O}{\|}}{C}-OCH_3 + HO- \quad \longrightarrow \quad -\overset{\overset{\displaystyle O}{\|}}{C}-O- \ + \ CH_3OH \qquad \text{(polyester)}$$

Table 10.1

	Water absorption immersion at 20°C %	Resistance to (at 20°C unless otherwise stated)								
		Boiling water	Mineral acids dilute	Mineral acids con-centrated	Alkalis	Alcohols	Ketones	Aromatic hydro-carbons	Chlorin-ated hydro-carbons	Olive oil
Acetal copolymer (oxymethylene copolymer)	0·8	good	fair	poor	excellent	excellent	good	excellent	good	excellent
Nylon 66	~9	fair[a]	fair	poor	good	fair[a]	fair[a]	fair[a]	fair[a]	excellent
Polypropylene	~0	excellent	excellent	good[b]	excellent	excellent	good	fair–poor	fair–poor	excellent
Polystyrene	~0	softens	excellent	good	excellent	fair	poor	poor	poor	fair–poor
PTFE	~0	excellent	excellent	excellent	excellent	excellent	excellent	excellent	excellent	excellent
PVC	~0	softens	excellent	excellent	excellent	excellent	fair	fair	fair	excellent

[a] May be absorbed giving plasticizing effect.
[b] Except with oxidizing acids.

The reactive groups may be part of the same, or different polymer molecules. Unfortunately the reaction is not 'one-way' and can proceed backwards under appropriate conditions, splitting the polymer chain and degrading the properties. Typical hydrolysis conditions which should, therefore, be avoided to retain good properties are heating to high temperatures in the presence of moisture, or treatment, especially at elevated temperatures, with alkalis or, more particularly, acids. The former restriction requires that hydrolysable plastics are scrupulously dry before heating during processing. Certain other plastics are also susceptible to hydrolysis: acetal plastics are perhaps the most important examples outside conventional condensation polymers. Plastics are largely organic materials and as such most are susceptible to oxidation under forcing conditions. Some aqueous solutions, particularly those of concentrated oxidizing acids, are powerful oxidizing agents and can affect plastics articles. For example, red fuming nitric acid at 80°C slowly erodes polyethylene although the process of dissolution takes many hours. Polypropylene is somewhat more readily attacked by such agents whilst polytetrafluoroethylene is immune to attack.

10.4 DEGRADATION

Whilst degradation is most commonly encountered as a consequence of chemical interaction of the plastics with its environment, breaking of molecular chains can also occur without the involvement of external chemical agencies under particular imposed conditions. Such conditions are most likely to be encountered during processing and a discussion of the phenomenon is included here since it is a factor which influences the properties of the final article. The breakdown of polymer chains is accelerated by high temperatures. There are three main regions of interest.

(1) Random scission occurs in many plastics but is particularly important in polyolefines at high processing temperatures.

(2) Chemical changes not primarily associated with the main chain, e.g. elimination of hydrogen chloride from PVC leaving an unsaturated residual chain susceptible to further chemical attack.

(3) Depolymerization or 'unzipping' reactions responsible for loss of monomer from the polymer, e.g. methyl methacrylate from its polymer and formaldehyde from polyoxymethylene.

Steps taken to minimize these largely unwanted reactions include the use of stabilizing additives and limitation of the temperatures to which the material is subjected.

10.4.1 Oxidative Degradation

It was noted in a previous section that plastics are susceptible to oxidation. Oxidation conditions frequently encountered are high temperatures in the presence of air, both during processing and in subsequent use. Deterioration under these conditions is known as thermal oxidation, and is a mechanism which affects most plastics at some stage. Fortunately, the oxidation process can be retarded by the incorporation of additives specific in any one polymer. These are generally termed antioxidants although different substances interfere with the oxidation process by different mechanisms. A number of theories have been postulated concerning the course of oxidation of organic polymers. In many cases, and certainly with polyolefines, (polyethylene, polypropylene, poly-4-methylpentene) the reaction is that of a hydrocarbon chain with oxygen. A common feature of all the theories and a fact established experimentally is that the oxidation process is a chain reaction, that is molecular species active in promoting oxidation are regenerated continuously by the oxidation process. Further, a particular intermediate, a hydroperoxide ($R\!-\!O_2H$) has been identified in many oxidation processes and it is likely to be a key intermediate in the reaction. On this basis two principal classes of antioxidants, those which disrupt the chain propagation step ('chain stoppers'), and those which react selectively with hydroperoxides ('hydroperoxide scavengers') can be distinguished. Each type of antioxidant has a marked effect on the oxidation process whilst together it is perhaps not surprising that synergism, that is, a more than additive effect, is observed. Examples of the two classes are phenols and sulphur-containing organic compounds respectively. Total antioxidant addition rarely exceeds 1% of the weight of the resin and is frequently $\frac{1}{5}$ or $\frac{1}{10}$ of this.

10.4.2 Resistance to Ultraviolet Radiation and Weathering

Very few organic polymers do not absorb radiation in the ultraviolet range of the spectrum. Absorption of such radiation implies that the molecule concerned has increased energy which in certain cases is sufficient to disrupt the molecule and in other cases for it to show enhanced reactivity particularly in the presence of oxygen. The energy of the radiation is related to frequency so that high-frequency radiation, i.e. ultraviolet radiation in the present case, is the most damaging. Sunlight contains a high proportion of high-frequency UV radiation and so might be expected to be more damaging to plastics than diffuse white light and this is indeed found to be so. Exposure of plastics to UV radiation from special sources indoors is an attempt to simulate exposure to sunlight so that accelerated tests, running 24 hours a day, can be employed to monitor the likely behaviour of plastics out of doors.

Various sources of UV radiation are in current use but it can be stated quite generally that none of these accurately reproduces the effects of natural weathering. Mercury discharge tubes are frequently employed and, more recently, filtered radiation from a xenon arc has found favour, since the intensity distribution with wavelength is very similar to that of sunlight in the UV region. However, quantitative correlations are by no means universally obtained between this equipment and natural weathering.

Minimizing the effect of exposure to UV radiation can be achieved either by preventing the radiation reaching the plastics material by internal screening or by providing an alternative, less damaging route for the dissipation of the energy of the radiation. Internal screening of the plastics material is most easily achieved by pigmentation: carbon black is one of the most effective additives in this sense. On the other hand, the damaging radiation is curtailed by exposing the plastics material behind glass. Additives which provide an alternative means of energy dissipation to degradation of the polymer chain are available commercially. Whilst conventional antioxidants are not particularly effective in reducing UV-initiated oxidation by themselves, their use in compositions containing a UV stabilizer can lead to a useful enhancement of UV resistance. As noted above, the UV constituent of weathering is likely to be the most destructive aspect of natural exposure. There are, however, other factors which may be of some importance for particular plastics in specific applications.

(1) Diurnal variation of temperature, leading to thermal expansion and contraction with consequent stresses built up and possibly resulting in fatigue.

(2) Periodic wetting of the sample followed by drying out. This may lead to internally generated stresses or the leaching out of water-soluble additives.

(3) Erosion of the surface by wind-borne grit or sand.

(4) In industrial regions, environmental attack on the material by atmospheric pollutants (e.g. SO_2).

10.5 FLAMMABILITY

As we have seen in section 10.4 plastics are degraded to smaller molecules under the action of intense heat. These products in turn might be expected to contribute generally to the fuel content of the system. Under less severe heating conditions thermoplastics soften and, in the presence of air, some burn, whilst others are resistant to burning.

Flammability tests are notoriously irreproducible; also there is frequently very poor correlation between laboratory tests and practical experience although closer attention to the details of test procedures is improving the situation somewhat. Under these circumstances, it is possible only to classify plastics' behaviour qualitatively. There are four aspects which require consideration: (i) ignition, (ii) tendency to continue burning: characteristics of burning, drips etc., (iii) emission of toxic or corrosive fumes or smoke during burning, and (iv) behaviour under pyrolysis conditions.

It is in respect of (i), (ii) and (iii) enumerated above that plastics differ amongst themselves and where changes can be brought about by appropriate formulation. A few examples illustrate the range of behaviour encountered in plastics.

Nitrocellulose plastics are highly inflammable.

Polyethylene and polypropylene burn like a hard wax.

Acrylics burn like hard wood, with burning drips.

Unplasticized PVC decomposes at temperatures above 200°C, liberating HCl which causes the flame to be extinguished.

PTFE does not burn but decomposes at temperatures above 400°C.

The flammability of thermoplastics depends on geometrical shape but the collapse of shape to a melt pool generally reduces the rate of burning, although the fuel value of such a melt pool in a burning building obviously contributes positively to the fuel content of the system. In many practical applications, ignition is perhaps the most crucial step (as in domestic electrical equipment). For this reason efforts are made to delay ignition to higher temperatures or longer times at a given temperature by suitable additives or design features.

10.6 PERMEABILITY

Plastics are low-density materials in consequence of their being comparatively 'open' structures. It is not surprising, therefore, that they allow the passage of small molecules through their structures to a greater or lesser extent, i.e. they are permeable. Water vapour is composed of such small molecules and water vapour permeability is an obviously important property of packaging materials, whilst permeation by oxygen, carbon dioxide and other materials is important in particular applications.

The permeability of a plastics material with respect to a particular fluid depends on many factors, including

(i) nature of the plastics material and the test fluid,
(ii) concentration of the test fluid (or partial pressure for a gas),
(iii) temperature,
(iv) time of permeation,
(v) area of plastics material exposed,
(vi) thickness of plastics material.

Table 10.2

	Permeability g/msPa			
	Water vapour	Oxygen	Carbon dioxide	Nitrogen
Poly 4-methylpentene	$4 \cdot 1 \times 10^{-12}$	$2 \cdot 6 \times 10^{-13}$	$9 \cdot 7 \times 10^{-13}$	$5 \cdot 9 \times 10^{-14}$
Polypropylene	$3 \cdot 1 \times 10^{-13}$	$2 \cdot 5 \times 10^{-14}$	$1 \cdot 4 \times 10^{-13}$	$4 \cdot 2 \times 10^{-15}$
Polyvinyl chloride	$1 \cdot 2 \times 10^{-12}$	$4 \cdot 5 \times 10^{-16}$	$1 \cdot 7 \times 10^{-15}$	$1 \cdot 4 \times 10^{-17}$
Polyvinylidene chloride	$1 \cdot 8 \times 10^{-14}$	$5 \cdot 1 \times 10^{-19}$	$1 \cdot 4 \times 10^{-18}$	$5 \cdot 9 \times 10^{-20}$
Polycarbonate	$8 \cdot 1 \times 10^{-12}$	$1 \cdot 8 \times 10^{-14}$	$1 \cdot 5 \times 10^{-13}$	$2 \cdot 8 \times 10^{-15}$
Polyamide (nylon 6)	$4 \cdot 1 - 41^{a} \times 10^{-13}$	$1 \cdot 0 \times 10^{-16}$	$1 \cdot 8 \times 10^{-15}$	$1 \cdot 7 \times 10^{-18}$

[a] Dependent on relative humidity.

Table 10.3 Conversion Table for Permeability Data

Column A	Column P	Column B
$\frac{1}{M} \times 2 \cdot 988 \times 10^{5}$	cm³ (STP) cm/cm² s (cmHg)	$M \times 3 \cdot 347 \times 10^{-6}$
$\frac{1}{M} \times 2 \cdot 988 \times 10^{6}$	cm³ (STP) mm/cm² s (cmHg)	$M \times 3 \cdot 347 \times 10^{-7}$
$\frac{1}{M} \times 1 \cdot 076 \times 10^{9}$	cm³ (STP) cm/cm² h (cmHg)	$M \times 9 \cdot 294 \times 10^{-10}$
$\frac{1}{M} \times 2 \cdot 582 \times 10^{10}$	cm³ (STP) cm/cm² d (cmHg)	$M \times 3 \cdot 873 \times 10^{-11}$
$\frac{1}{M} \times 8 \cdot 175 \times 10^{10}$	cm³ (STP) cm/cm² h atm	$M \times 1 \cdot 223 \times 10^{-11}$
$\frac{1}{M} \times 1 \cdot 962 \times 10^{12}$	cm³ (STP) cm/cm² d atm	$M \times 5 \cdot 097 \times 10^{-13}$
$\frac{1}{M} \times 1 \cdot 962 \times 10^{18}$	cm³ (STP) 0·1 mm/m² d atm	$M \times 5 \cdot 097 \times 10^{-19}$
$\frac{1}{M} \times 4 \cdot 982 \times 10^{17}$	cm³ (STP) ml/100 in² d atm	$M \times 2 \cdot 007 \times 10^{-18}$
$\frac{1}{M} \times 1 \cdot 962 \times 10^{16}$	cm³ (STP) 0·1 mm/dm² d atm	$M \times 5 \cdot 097 \times 10^{-17}$
$\frac{1}{M} \times 2 \cdot 988 \times 10^{4}$	cm³ (STP) cm/cm² s torr	$M \times 3 \cdot 347 \times 10^{-5}$
10^{6}	μg m/Ns	1×10^{-6}
10^{2}	kg/m s bar	1×10^{-2}
10^{5}	g/m s bar	1×10^{-5}
$1 \cdot 152 \times 10^{7}$	g/m d torr	$8 \cdot 680 \times 10^{-8}$
$2 \cdot 451 \times 10^{5}$	lb/ft h atm	$4 \cdot 080 \times 10^{-4}$
$1 \cdot 693 \times 10^{6}$	grain/ft h mbar	$5 \cdot 907 \times 10^{-7}$
$6 \cdot 881 \times 10^{8}$	grain in/ft² h (inHg)	$1 \cdot 453 \times 10^{-8}$

M is the molecular weight of the penetrant (in grams).
To convert data in g/msPa to units in column P, use the multipliers in column A.
To convert data in units in column P to g/msPa, use the multipliers in column B.

Thus for a given plastics/fluid combination the quantity of fluid permeating (q) is given by

$$q = \frac{PtA(p_1 - p_2)}{l}$$

where P is the permeability coefficient; t is time of permeation; A is sample area; l is sample thickness, and p_1, p_2 are the partial pressures of fluid on the two sides of the sample. The permeability coefficient is expressed in g/msPa requiring that t be measured in seconds, A and l be expressed in m^2 and m respectively; p_1 and p_2 are in Pascals (N/m²) and q is in g. Some representative data are given in Table 10.2 and conversion factors to and from a wide variety of units are presented in Table 10.3.

Permeability is a steady-state concept and is applicable generally to transport of penetrant through thin films. For plastics of thicker section where the establishment of steady-state conditions takes a substantial time compared with the design lifetime of the component, it may not be sufficient to consider only the steady-state permeability but to examine the problem in greater detail in terms of the solubility and diffusion coefficients. More advanced texts should be consulted for further information for non-steady-state conditions.

10.6.1 Absorption and Desorption

The process by which fluid is absorbed or desorbed by a plastics material is time-dependent, governed by its solubility and by the diffusion coefficient. The time scales to equilibrium may be surprisingly long; for example nylon 66, thickness 3 mm, immersed in water requires over a year to reach equilibrium absorption of some 8·3%. A similar sample of poly(methyl methacrylate) requires approximately twice as long to reach its saturation value of some 2·15% moisture. The property governing the absorption/desorption behaviour is the diffusion coefficient and to obtain an appreciation of the time scales of these processes the half-life of the process $t_{1/2}$ is given by

$$t_{1/2} = \frac{0·04919 . l^2}{D}$$

where l is the thickness (assumed to be penetrated from one side) and D is the diffusion coefficient. For example, for moisture in poly(methyl methacrylate) D is $0·3 \times 10^{-12}$ m²/s, and for a sheet 3 mm thickness wetted from one side only, $t_{1/2}$ becomes $17\frac{1}{2}$ days. By its nature, the absorption rate decreases as saturation is approached so that equilibrium absorption in this example takes a very long time indeed, as noted above.

10.7   FURTHER READING

BS 4618, *Recommendations for the Presentation of Plastics Design Data*, Part 4.1, 'Chemical resistance'; Part 4.2, 'Weathering', British Standards Institution.

R. J. Conley (Ed.), *Thermal Stability of Polymer*, Vol. 1, Dekker, New York, 1970.

J. Crank, *Mathematics of Diffusion*, Oxford, 1957.

J. Crank and G. S. Park (Eds.), *Diffusion in Polymers*, Academic Press, 1968.

W. Jost, *Diffusion in Solids, Liquids, Gases*, Academic Press, 1952.

L. Reich and S. S. Stivala, *Autoxidation of Hydrocarbons and Polymers*, Dekker, New York, 1969.

G. Scott, *Atmospheric Oxidation and Antioxidants*, Elsevier, 1965.

11

Processing Methods and Properties of Thermoplastics Melts

by P. C. Powell

11.1 PROCESSING METHODS

In the context of engineering design, a material which is thought likely to fulfil a given function is seldom chosen on the basis of its mechanical properties alone. In particular, if the material cannot be fabricated easily and economically into the required shape and form, its usefulness is very limited indeed. An understanding of the main processing methods and the properties of thermoplastics melts should therefore help the designer to exploit fully the materials and the processing machinery used in thermoplastics technology.[1]

The first section of this chapter describes the main manufacturing methods for producing finished or semi-finished thermoplastics articles from raw materials, highlighting the chief features of the equipment and the procedure with its advantages and disadvantages. The rest of the chapter is given over to a phenomenological discussion of the physics of thermoplastics melts in which the extremes of analytical rigour have been sacrificed in order to develop tractable design methods: these methods have been used successfully to resolve many practical processing problems, including the design of moulds and dies, and the assessment of the ability of a given machine to produce the required product.

There is a wide range of techniques by which plastics articles may be produced. Certainly it is possible to machine and weld or cement most thermoplastics. Of greater significance to the designer of plastics components and articles, however, are the more common and more widely used methods of manufacture (in particular the various kinds of moulding) which often enable parts of complicated shape and intricate detail to be made in one operation with little or no further post fabrication requirement.

11.1.1   Extrusion

Extrusion[2,3] is an important process by which about 60% of all thermoplastics are converted into a wide range of products including pipe and profiles (of particular interest to the mechanical engineer), wire coverings for electrical insulation, sheet for subsequent shaping and fabrication, and film for packaging.

In the basic extrusion line an Archimedean screw is used to transfer the feedstock through a heated cylinder (the barrel) to the die; in the barrel the thermoplastic is compacted and mixed by the screw, and the material softens as a result of the frictional heating arising from the shearing action of the screw and also by heat transfer from the hot barrel walls. The soft material conforms to the shape of the die, but the dimensions of the cooled product depend on the cooling and haul-off conditions.

Extrusion produces long lengths of constant cross-section, for which the cost of the die can be only a small proportion of the total manufacturing cost. In contrast, the cost of the extruder and auxiliary equipment can be high, and finishing or post-fabrication assembly operations (e.g. welding or cementing of sheet) may often be required.

11.1.2   Injection Moulding

More than 25% of all thermoplastics raw materials are processed by injection moulding into articles of a wide variety of shapes (which can be complicated), in sizes ranging from a few millimetres maximum dimension to mechanical handling pallets 1200 mm × 1000 mm × 150 mm.

Injection moulding[4,5] is, by and large, the plastics equivalent of metals pressure die casting. The raw material is melted by passing through a heated cylinder, and a predetermined quantity of molten material is then rapidly injected at high pressure to fill the mould completely. The simplest mould[5-7] usually oil- or water-cooled, consists of two parts, one male and the other female, which define a cavity when closed. Injection moulding confers the advantages that articles are moulded to the required shape and size with repeatable precision (without the need for further finishing operations), features such as inserts, threads and holes can be moulded in, and high output rates can be achieved. In contrast, the capital cost of equipment can be high because the heating cylinder must resist high internal pressures, and the mould locking force must be adequate, to prevent material escaping from the mating faces. Furthermore, mould costs can be high compared with those for other moulding processes, because the mould must be robust to withstand high injection pressures without undue distortion; precision engineering is involved to obtain the desired cavity shape.

11.1.3 Blow Moulding

Blow moulding[8] is a method of producing hollow articles in a variety of shapes which can be complicated and in sizes varying from spheres 10 mm diameter to tanks of 2000 litre capacity. The simplest mould, which is located beneath an extruder, consists of two female parts which contain a cavity when closed. A vertical tube, or 'parison' is extruded between the sections of the open mould. The mould is closed and the parison is inflated pneumatically to conform with the surface of the mould.

The outside dimensions of the blow-moulded articles are accurately determined, mould costs can be low (because only low inflation pressures are used), threads and heavy texture finishes can be moulded on the outside surfaces, and large open-ended parts can be made by splitting a closed moulding. However, the designer should bear in mind that it is not easy to mould-in lugs, bosses or holes; that close tolerances are obtained only on the outer wall; and that the wall thickness decreases with increasing mould diameter (and hence thinning occurs at corners and the thinnest wall normally occurs at the largest diameter). Furthermore, cooling times can be longer, compared with those for injection moulded articles of the same material and section thickness, because blow mouldings are normally cooled from the outside only.

11.1.4 Rotational Moulding

Rotational moulding, like blow moulding, produces hollow three-dimensional articles, but usually of simple shape, in sizes ranging normally from small footballs to 3 m³ capacity tanks.

The simplest mould consists of two female parts. The cold mould is filled with a predetermined weight of powder and then slowly rotated about two perpendicular axes in an oven. When all the thermoplastics material has melted and conformed to the shape of the mould, the mould is transferred, still rotating, to a cooling bay and the moulding is cooled to a temperature at which it is form stable and can be removed from the mould.

Because moulds do not have to resist internal pressure, the mould costs are low and delivery times for the light-duty constructions tend to be short even for large moulds, compared with those for blow moulding tools. All the raw material is converted into the finished moulding; the wall thickness is more nearly constant than can normally be obtained by blow moulding; foamed and multi-layer walls can be made; bosses, lugs and metal inserts can be moulded-in and open-ended parts can be made by splitting a closed moulding. However, cycle times are much longer than for parts of corresponding thicknesses made by other moulding operations because the raw material has to be heated in the mould from cold and from the outside of the mould. Moreover, raw materials are generally in the form of powders because these fuse more rapidly than would granules: raw material costs for powders are higher where particle size reduction costs have to be met. The designer should bear in mind that only outside dimensions can be held to close tolerances, that there is a limited choice of materials suitable for processing by rotational moulding, and that holes cannot be moulded-in but must be formed in a post-moulding operation.

11.1.5 Thermoforming

The thermoforming process produces from thermoplastics sheet hollow or shaped articles ranging in size from small dairy-produce containers to dinghy hulls and car bodies. To make thermoformed articles it is necessary to have a means of heating and softening the thermoplastics sheet (generally in a thermostatically controlled oven) and a means of making the softened sheet conform to the required shape. In addition, it may be necessary to have a mould. The shaping pressure can be applied by using a simple plunger, or by introducing an air pressure difference by means of a vacuum[9] or compressed air supply. The best possible wall-thickness distribution in the final shaping may result from a judicious combination of pressure and vacuum forming, with or without some form of mechanical pressure.

Because tools do not have to withstand high temperatures and pressures, inexpensive equipment can be used, and thermoforming lends itself to the production of large thin-walled parts which could not be produced economically or technically by moulding. However, the 'raw material' is in a semi-fabricated sheet form which is more expensive than, for example, granules or powder, post-shaping trimming operations are generally required and these produce scrap, and cycle times tend to be long. The designer should also remember that thinning occurs, particularly at corners, the amount of thinning depending on the draw-down.

11.1.6 Production of Foamed Structures

Articles can be made in which the thermoplastic has a fine cellular structure. The two main ways of achieving this structure are to incorporate a blowing agent with the base polymer so that gas is released when the mixture is heated to a certain temperature, or to cause two chemicals to react to produce the polymer and the gas at the same time. There are basically two types of foam: flexible foam and rigid structural foam. Foam sandwiches consist of a foamed plastics core faced with solid skins of the same or of a different material. Articles made from rigid structural thermoplastics foams have a high stiffness per unit weight; this feature is most pronounced where the structure consists of foam sandwich elements.

Foams can be made by three main types of process: moulding, extrusion and casting. In the low-pressure injection moulding process[10] foam is generated by release of pressure as the melt enters the mould cavity: cheap moulds can be used but cycle times can be long, and the surface of mouldings usually shows a swirl pattern.

In the high-pressure injection moulding process the melt is compressed within the mould and subsequently allowed to foam by enlargement of the mould cavity; compared with the low pressure process, mouldings have a better surface finish, but mould costs are higher. A development of the high-pressure technique is the ICI sandwich moulding process,[11] which can be used to produce a foam-sandwich structure. The process uses conventional injection moulding equipment and pressures, thus enabling large-area thin mouldings to be made. Extruded thermoplastic foams can be produced by free or controlled expansion of a hot mixture of plastic and blowing agent through an orifice.[12]

One casting procedure is based largely on rotational moulding technology: the tool is filled with a predetermined quantity of granular or powder reactants and then heated to a temperature sufficiently high to fuse the charge and decompose the blowing agents. The tool is then cooled to a temperature at which further blowing will not occur when the article is removed. Another casting procedure relies on the use of a liquid or partially frothed foam: when the foam has cured sufficiently to be handled without damage, it is removed from the tool.

11.1.7 Other Techniques

There are many other processes used to convert plastics raw materials into finished components, but in general they are of more limited interest. They include:

Calendering:[13] a process for making thin films and sheets by squeezing hot thermoplastic materials through rollers.

Coating: using powders, solutions, or dispersions. Dipping, brushing, spraying, roller-coating, knife-coating and fluidized bed coating are all employed. Coatings can be used to protect metals and to produce composite plastics/fabric and plastics/paper flexible sheet (e.g. leathercloth).

Impregnating: porous materials such as fabrics and papers are dipped into baths of liquids, solutions or dispersions. Excess of liquid is usually removed by rollers, and the impregnated material is then dried and, if necessary, cured, i.e. gelled, cross-linked, etc.

Laminating: sheets or plies of thermoplastics or of a material impregnated with a thermoplastic are pressed and heated between flat parallel platens. The plastic fluxes and forms a uniform matrix. It is also possible to make rods and tubes by this method.

Casting: the liquid raw material is charged to a mould where it is polymerized to form a solid moulding. Acrylic and nylon (particularly type 6) mouldings can be produced by this method.

Machining:[14] block, rod and other blanks can be drilled, milled and turned using methods closely resembling those used with metals.

Fabrication of PTFE: PTFE cannot be processed by conventional methods such as injection moulding and melt extrusion because it has no truly fluid state. It is necessary to compact the powder (raw material) and sinter at a high temperature to produce a continuous structure in a specific shape.

11.2 PROPERTIES OF THERMOPLASTICS MELTS

11.2.1 Viscous Behaviour: Basic Concepts

When thermoplastics melts are being processed, they are subjected to forces which affect the shape of the material. To transfer data relating forces, deformations and deformation rates from one set of dimensions, e.g. small laboratory rheometers, to another, e.g. extruder dies or injection moulds of full-scale processing equipment, it is necessary to have a basic understanding of these processes. Concepts such as stress, strain, strain rate, viscosity and elasticity are of fundamental importance, and are the basis of this understanding and of the scientific design of processing equipment.[15-18]

Three types of stress are of interest: shear, tensile and bulk (hydrostatic tension or compression). Stress is defined as force per unit area of cross-section. Shear stresses are produced by equal and opposite parallel forces which make adjacent planes slide over each other, and calculation of shear stresses is based on the cross-sectional area parallel to the direction of the applied force. Tensile stresses are set up across plane sections perpendicular to the direction of the applied force. The nominal tensile stress, appropriate for small deformations, is defined as load/original area. For large deformations 'true stress' is used and is defined as load/cross-sectional area at a given deformation.

Of the three stress systems, shear stresses (τ) are normally of greatest importance in the processing of thermoplastics, because these determine the magnitudes of pressure drops in extrusion dies and in sprues, runners and cavities in injection moulding, and hence the power requirements and the associated efficiencies of processing equipment. Tensile stresses (σ) can also assume importance, often combined with shear stresses, for example in the draw-down of extrudates in blow moulding, and in fibre production, in the inflation of tubes during blow moulding or of bubbles in tubular film production, and in injection moulding during the spreading disc flow from gates (injection points) into a cavity. Compression resulting from hydrostatic stresses is often considered negligible, although the effect of hydrostatic stresses on other properties, for example on melt viscosity, can be considerable and important.

Associated with these stresses are changes in shape expressed as strain. For shear deformation, strain is defined as the displacement of two parallel planes unit distance apart. For small tensile deformations engineering strain is defined as change in length per unit length; for the large tensile deformations which obtain during most processing operations, strain is defined as the natural logarithm of (changed dimension/original dimension), often termed 'true strain'.

Strain rate in shear, usually termed the 'shear rate', is defined as the difference in velocity between two parallel plates unit distance apart. For streamline flow in a capillary of radius R the shear rate at the die wall, $\dot{\gamma}$, corresponding to a volume flow rate Q is derived from simple fluid theory as

$$\dot{\gamma} = 4Q/\pi R^3 \tag{11.1}$$

For streamline flow in a channel of slot profile, width T and thickness H, the shear rate is

$$\dot{\gamma} = 6Q/TH^2 \tag{11.2}$$

In extruder dies shear rates in the range 10 to 10^3 s^{-1} are common; in injection moulding the shear rates are much higher, normally in the range 10^3 to 10^5 s^{-1}.

The behaviour of thermoplastics melts is viscoelastic and can be qualitatively represented as a Maxwell model with variable coefficients. In any process the strain resulting from an applied stress consists of an irrecoverable viscous component and a recoverable elastic component.

Newton expressed the relationship between stress and strain rate in terms of their ratio, viscosity, which is a quantitative measure of the resistance to viscous deformation. The shear viscosity η is then given by

$$\eta = \tau/\dot{\gamma} \tag{11.3}$$

Thermoplastics melts have viscosities in the range 10–10^7 Ns/m^2. For tensile stresses the corresponding tensile viscosity λ is given by

$$\lambda = \sigma/\dot{\varepsilon} \tag{11.4}$$

where $\dot{\varepsilon}$ = tensile strain rate.

When a melt deforms in a viscous manner, the energy is dissipated as heat; for viscous flow in a capillary the associated average temperature rise, ΔT, is given approximately by

$$\Delta T = \frac{\Delta P}{\rho C_p} + \Delta P \left(\frac{\partial T}{\partial P} \right)_s \tag{11.5}$$

where ΔP = pressure drop in capillary; ρ = melt density; C_p = specific heat at constant pressure; $(\partial T/\partial P)_s$ = rate of change of temperature with pressure at constant entropy. (See also Chapter 8.)

11.2.1.1 *Shear Viscosity*

The concept of a Newtonian fluid (in which viscosity does not depend on shear rate) is a cornerstone of classical fluid mechanics. Many texts discuss the behaviour of such fluids (e.g. water) and give equations for predicting pressure drops (which determine pumping requirements) associated with the flow of Newtonian fluids through pipes and along ducts and channels. These texts also discuss the difference between, and the importance of, the inter-relationship between viscous and inertial forces, often in terms of the Reynolds number (Re) defined by the equation:

$$Re = \frac{\bar{v}\rho D}{\eta} \tag{11.6}$$

where ρ = fluid density; $\bar{v}$ = average fluid velocity; D = pipe diameter; η = coefficient of viscosity of the fluid.

For Newtonian fluids flow in pipes is normally laminar for $Re < 2100$, and normally turbulent for $Re > 2500$. The Reynolds number in thermoplastics processing operations is commonly less than 10.

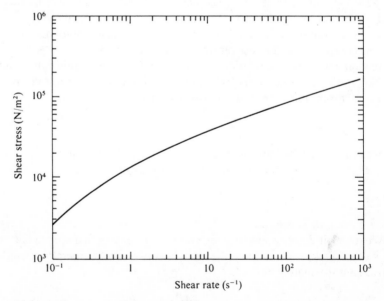

Figure 11.1 Typical curve of shear stress vs. shear rate for a low-density polyethylene ('Alkathene' XDG 33 at 210°C, atmospheric pressure)

Most thermoplastics melts only exhibit Newtonian behaviour at shear rates far below those of practical importance. At shear rates achieved in most processing methods, the shear rate increases much more rapidly than the shear stress. Materials which behave in this manner are termed 'pseudo-plastic'†, or 'shear thinning' and the ratio of shear stress to shear rate is then termed 'apparent shear viscosity'. Values of apparent shear viscosity corresponding to shear rates encountered in extrusion and in injection moulding are normally in the range $10–10^4$ Ns/m^2. At viscosities higher than about 10^4 Ns/m^2 normal extrusion becomes extremely difficult, and special techniques are required, e.g. pressure sintering of PTFE. At the low end of the scale, plastisols (for applications such as dip and knife coating) have viscosities of the order of 1 Ns/m^2. The rheology of materials with very high and very low viscosities will not be discussed in this chapter.

Viscosity data for plastics melts under simple shear may be obtained from measurements made using a conventional cone-and-plate technique[19] for low shear stresses and a capillary extrusion technique for high stresses. For a

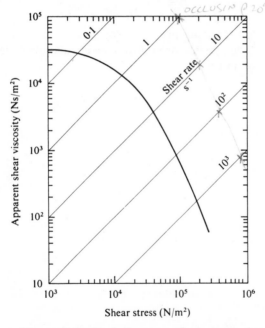

Figure 11.2 Typical curve of apparent shear viscosity vs. shear stress for a low-density polyethylene ('Alkathene' XDG 33 at 210°C, atmospheric pressure)

† The term 'pseudo-plastic' (decrease in viscosity with increase in shear *rate*) should not be confused with 'thixotropic' (decrease in viscosity with increase in *duration* of shear).

Newtonian fluid the apparent shear rate at the die wall $\dot{\gamma}$ may be calculated from equation (11.1). The data may be presented as a curve of log shear stress/log shear rate, as shown for a low-density polyethylene at 210°C and at atmspheric pressure in Figure 11.1.

The same data are, however, more commonly presented in two other ways. They may be presented as curves of log apparent viscosity/log shear stress at a particular temperature and hydrostatic pressure as shown in Figure 11.2. Since shear rate is the ratio of stress to apparent viscosity, it is possible to superpose lines of constant shear rate on Figure 11.2. The other representation of the data is as a curve of log apparent viscosity/log shear rate, as shown in Figure 11.3. For a Newtonian fluid the log apparent viscosity/log shear rate curve would be a horizontal straight line, but for pseudo-plastic materials the apparent viscosity decreases with increasing shear rate.

The shear stress is related to the pressure drop P_L through a capillary tube of length L, radius R by

$$\tau = \frac{(P_L - P_0)\,R}{2L} \tag{11.7}$$

where P_0 is the corresponding pressure drop through a die of zero length. The dependence of the pressure drop through a circular die of zero length on shear stress is shown in Figure 11.4.

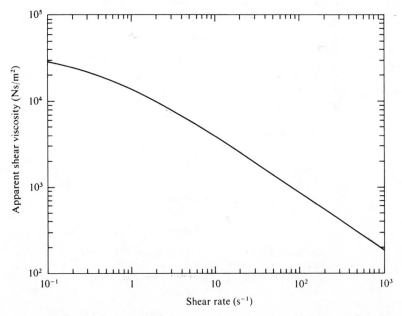

Figure 11.3 Typical curve of apparent shear viscosity vs. shear rate for a low-density polyethylene ('Alkathene' XDG 33 at 210°C, atmospheric pressure)

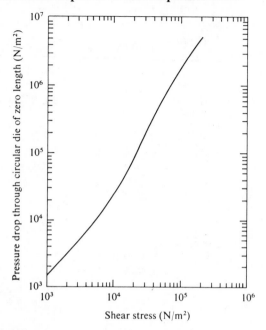

Figure 11.4 The dependence on shear stress of the pressure drop through a circular die of zero length ('Alkathene' XDG 33 at 170°C, atmospheric pressure)

Figure 11.5 presents shear viscosity data for five materials at their normal processing temperatures. It can be seen that at low shear stresses the behaviour is virtually Newtonian, whereas at higher stresses the behaviour can be markedly pseudo-plastic.

Several attempts have been made to describe pseudo-plastic behaviour mathematically by deriving functions to fit the experimental data: the most useful of these is the 'power-law equation', which takes the form

$$\tau = C\dot{\gamma}^n \qquad (11.8)$$

where C and n are 'constants' for a given material under given conditions. From the definition of apparent viscosity, it follows that

$$\eta = C\dot{\gamma}^{n-1} \qquad (11.9)$$

For plastics melts, curves of log apparent viscosity/log shear rate can often be approximated by straight line over one–two decades of shear rate, the slope of which is $n - 1$. The value of C, which seldom has any usefulness in itself, is the value of apparent viscosity projected to unit shear rate.

Table 11.1. Values of Power Law Index, n, for Six Materials

Shear rate	Polymethyl methacrylate ('Diakon', MG)	Acetal copolymer ('Kematal', M90)	Type 6,6 nylon ('Maranyl', A100)	Propylene/ethylene copolymer ('Propathene', GSE108)	Low-density polyethylene ('Alkathene', XDG33)	Unplasticized PVC ('Welvic', R7/622)
s^{-1}	230°C	200°C	285°C	230°C	170°C	150°C
10^{-1}	—	—	—	0·93	0·7	—
1	1·00	1·00	—	0·66	0·44	—
10	0·82	1·00	0·96	0·46	0·32	0·62
10^2	0·46	0·80	0·91	0·34	0·26	0·55
10^3	0·22	0·42	0·71	0·19	—	0·47
10^4	0·18	0·18	0·40	0·15	—	—
10^5	—	—	0·28	—	—	—

For a Newtonian fluid $n = 1$; for thermoplastics the lower the value of n the more pseudo-plastic is the melt. Typical values of the power-law index, n, for thermoplastics melts covering a range of shear rates are given in Table 11.1.

At this juncture it is worth commenting further on the calculation of shear rate. Equation (11.1) assumes that the fluid has a parabolic velocity profile. Thermoplastics melts are strongly pseudo-plastic and, for flow in a capillary, it is theoretically necessary[15] to apply the Rabinowitsch correction $4n/(3n + 1)$ to equation (11.1). Since n can be lower than 0·2, the difference between corrected and uncorrected values of shear rate can be greater than a factor of two, and this difference can lead to a difference of almost 20% in the relationship between shear stress and shear rate. If the Rabinowitsch correction is applied to the calculation of flow data, it follows that the same correction must be made in reverse when designing dies, with an enormous increase in algebraic

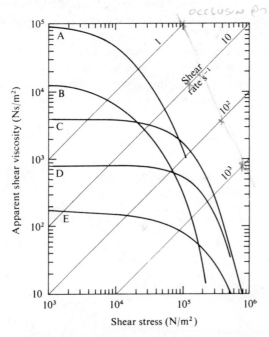

Figure 11.5 Typical curves of apparent shear viscosity vs. shear stress for five thermoplastics (at atmospheric pressure). A. Extrusion grade, low-density polyethylene at 170°C ('Alkathene' XDG 33). B. Extrusion grade, propylene/ethylene copolymer at 230°C ('Propathene' GSE 108). C. Moulding grade acrylic at 230°C ('Diakon' MG). D. Moulding grade acetal copolymer at 200°C ('Kematal' M90). E. Moulding grade nylon at 285°C ('Maranyl' A100)

complexity. We have found that since these two sets of cumbersome corrections largely cancel each other, the data and the die design methods in this chapter do not need to include the Rabinowitsch correction.

The balance of advantage between the particular materials shown in Figure 11.5 depends on the process conditions (and also on factors described in other chapters of this book). Compression moulding is a very low rate process; nylon 66 has the lowest viscosity under these conditions and would mould more easily than low-density polyethylene. In blow moulding, however, the melt must be form-stable to minimize parison draw-down and polyethylene, having the higher viscosity, would be better. Simple extrusion processes commonly take place at a shear rate of between 10 and 100 s^{-1}; in this range nylon is the easiest to process but will be least form-stable and the acrylic polymer the most difficult. Turning to injection moulding, where very high rates in excess of 10^3 s^{-1} are involved, nylon and polypropylene are the easiest to fabricate, polypropylene being easier to mould at shear rates greater than about 2000 s^{-1}.

The comparisons in the previous paragraph have, however, ignored the fact that viscosity depends on temperature and on hydrostatic pressure. An increase in temperature reduces the apparent shear viscosity as shown in Figure 11.6. The log viscosity/log shear stress curve at different temperatures

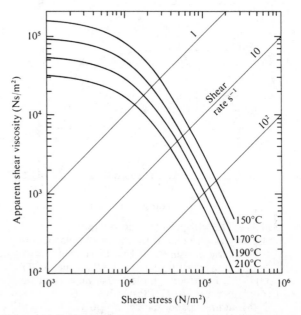

Figure 11.6 Typical curves showing the temperature dependence of the apparent shear viscosity of a low-density polyethylene ('Alkathene' XDG 33, atmospheric pressure)

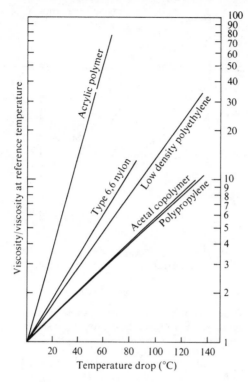

Figure 11.7 Melt viscosity at constant stress
and pressure as a function of temperature

can, to a good approximation, be superposed by a shift along the log viscosity axis. Increasing the temperature by 40°C decreases the viscosity of low-density polyethylene at constant stress (and constant pressure) by a factor of about 3. Data indicating the temperature dependence of melt viscosity at constant stress and pressure are presented in Figure 11.7. It will be seen that acrylics are far more sensitive to temperature changes than polypropylene, and a considerably reduced resistance to flow can be expected, resulting from heat generated during deformation, for the former.

An increase in hydrostatic pressure increases the apparent shear viscosity, as shown in Figure 11.8. The log viscosity/log shear stress curves can also be superposed by a shift along the log viscosity axis. Increasing the hydrostatic pressure from atmospheric (100 kN/m²) to about 100 MN/m² (a pressure commonly encountered in injection moulding) increases the viscosity of acetal copolymer at constant temperature and at constant stress by about 2·5. Data indicating the pressure dependence of melt viscosity at constant stress and temperature are presented in Figure 11.9.

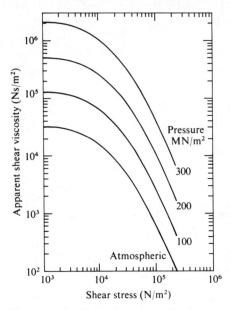

Figure 11.8 Typical curves showing the pressure dependence of the apparent shear viscosity of a low-density polyethylene ('Alkathene' XDG 33, at 210°C)

By comparison between Figures 11.8 and 11.9 it will be seen that the magnitude of the effects of probable variation in pressure on the viscosity at pressures of the order of 100 MN/m² are likely to be as great as, or maybe considerably greater than, those produced by potential variations in temperature. In this respect it is possible to express the effect of an increase in pressure in terms of the equivalent drop in temperature necessary to maintain constant viscosity, as shown in Figure 11.10.

It will be apparent that, at any constant value of shear stress, the value of the power-law index is independent of temperature and hydrostatic pressure but, at constant shear rate, n can vary appreciably. The value of C depends markedly on temperature and on the hydrostatic pressure to which the melt is subjected.

The discussion of shear viscosity has been restricted to the effect of stress, temperature and hydrostatic pressure on the behaviour of thermoplastics melts. Different grades of a given polymer can of course have quite different rheological properties; for unfilled thermoplastics the principal factors are molecular weight and molecular weight distribution. All other things being equal, the higher the molecular weight, the higher the apparent shear viscosity. At low stresses the apparent shear viscosity is directly proportional to molecular

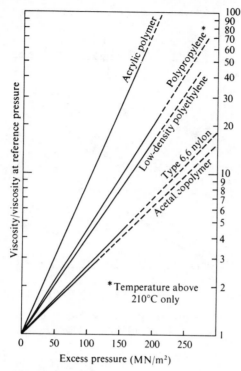

Figure 11.9 Melt viscosity at constant stress
and temperature as a function of pressure

weight raised to a power of about 3·5. At high stresses, high molecular weight
materials are usually more pseudo-plastic than their lower molecular weight
counterparts. Materials such as polyethylene, polypropylene and polyacetal
are often described commercially in terms of their melt flow index (MFI).
The melt flow index,[20] a measure of fluidity at low stress under carefully
prescribed conditions, is inversely proportional to shear viscosity and hence
related inversely to molecular weight.

For a given molecular weight, a thermoplastic with a broad molecular weight
distribution is more pseudo-plastic at low stresses than one of narrow distribution, but at high stresses the broad molecular weight distribution material
may be less pseudo-plastic.

11.2.1.2 *Tensile Viscosity*

At low stress (e.g. where shear behaviour is virtually Newtonian) thermoplastics melts behave in the manner first described by Trouton, i.e. the tensile
viscosity is independent of stress and equal to three times the viscosity under
simple shear. Tensile viscosity data for thermoplastics melts at high stresses

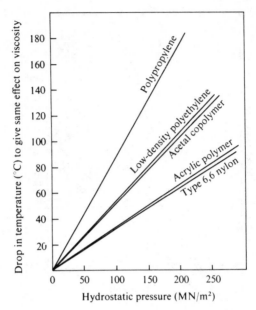

Figure 11.10 Temperature/pressure equivalence
for constant viscosity

may be obtained from measurements made using a constant stress melt tensile rheometer or by studies of converging flows.[21, 25] Data are normally presented as a curve of log tensile viscosity/log tensile stress, as shown for five materials in Figure 11.11.

For some materials the tensile viscosity is independent of stress even at high stress. For example acrylic, nylon 66 polymers and linear acetal co-polymers show such behaviour up to stresses of 1 MN/m^2. For other materials (e.g. polypropylene and high-density polyethylene) the viscosity decreases, sometimes to a plateau, as the stress is increased (tension-thinning). For the polypropylene shown in Figure 11.11, the value of tensile viscosity at a stress of 1 MN/m^2 is only one-fifth that at a stress of 1 kn/m^2. For a third class of material (e.g. branched polyolefines such as low-density polyethylene) the tensile viscosity increases to a plateau as the stress is increased (tension stiffening). For the low-density polyethylene shown in Figure 11.11, the value of tensile viscosity at a stress of 1 MN/m^2 is twice that at a stress of 1 kN/m^2, but the tensile viscosity of other low-density polyethylenes can increase by an order of magnitude, apparently depending on the same molecular features (e.g. branching) which control density. It can be seen from Figures 11.5 and 11.11 that there can be a difference of several orders of magnitude between tensile and shear viscosities at the same stress. There is no reason to assume that the dependence of tensile viscosity at a given shear stress on temperature

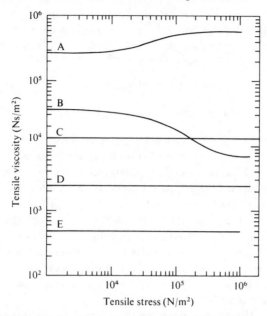

Figure 11.11 Typical curves of tensile viscosity vs. tensile stress for five thermoplastics at atmospheric pressure. A. Extrusion grade low-density polyethylene 170°C ('Alkathene' XDG 33). B. Extrusion grade propylene/ethylene copolymer, 230°C ('Propathene' GSE 108). C. Moulding grade acrylic, 230°C ('Diakon' MG). D. Moulding grade acetal copolymer, 200°C ('Kematal' M90). E. Moulding grade nylon 66 ('Maranyl' A100) 285°C

and on hydrostatic pressure is other than similar to that of shear viscosity, for which details are given in Figures 11.8–11.10.

The qualitative differences in tensile behaviour of different materials at high stress are directly relevant to dimensional stability where tensile stresses are induced by processing (e.g. parison sag or inflation, and casting of film). If tensile viscosity increases with increase in stress, then any local weakness or stress concentration becomes smoothed out and the deformation is uniform. Alternatively, if viscosity decreases with increase in stress, then local thin spots or stress concentrations will enhance the reduction in viscosity and the material may eventually rupture.

11.2.2 Elastic Behaviour: Basic Concepts

The discussion so far has centred on the viscous component of behaviour where melts are subjected to a constant stress. The melt can also store strain energy and, on removal of the stress, the elastic component of the strain can be recovered, following the concept of a Maxwell body with variable co-efficients. The ratio of stress to recoverable elastic strain is defined as the elastic modulus.

$$\text{Elastic shear modulus, } G = \tau/\gamma_R \tag{11.10}$$

$$\text{Elastic tensile modulus, } E = \gamma/\varepsilon_R \tag{11.11}$$

where γ_R = recoverable shear strain and ε_R = recoverable tensile strain.

In this chapter the use of the term 'modulus' refers to the elastic behaviour after the stress has been removed, and corresponds to the spring behaviour of the Maxwell model of linear viscoelasticity. In descriptions of linear elastic mechanical behaviour the term modulus refers to the ratio of stress to resultant strain; in Chapter 3 the term modulus usually refers to time-dependent low-strain behaviour during the period of application of a stress or strain.

A well-known example of elastic recovery is post-extrusion swelling. The relationship between swelling ratio (extrudate dimension/die dimension) and the elastic recoverable shear strain γ_R corresponding to the shear stress at the die wall will be discussed below.

At low stresses the elastic shear moduli of melts is in the range 1–1000 kN/m². At high stresses the upper limit to recoverable shear strain is normally about 6, and that of recoverable tensile strain about 2.

11.2.2.1   *Shear Elasticity*

A melt will deform continuously under stress but, when the stress is removed some deformation may be recovered elastically. If a thermoplastic melt is subjected to a constant low stress, it is found from experiments with a cone-and-plate rheometer that the ratio of stress to recoverable strain is a constant. At the higher stresses which occur in processing, and which are usually examined experimentally by post extrusion (die) swelling,[22] the recoverable shear strain tends to a limiting value of about 6 units of shear. Shear elasticity data are presented as curves of log elastic shear modulus/log shear stress, as shown for six thermoplastics melts in Figure 11.12. The same data may also be presented as curves of log recoverable shear strain/log stress (Figure 11.13); this facilitates the manual extraction of data for calculations of such features as swelling ratio.

Compared with viscosity, the elastic shear modulus appears to vary little with changes in temperature, hydrostatic pressure and molecular weight. Elasticity does, however, depend markedly on molecular weight distribution. Materials with a wide molecular weight distribution have a relatively low modulus and exhibit large, but tardy, recovery, whereas materials with a narrow molecular weight distribution have a much higher modulus and show a smaller but more rapid recovery.

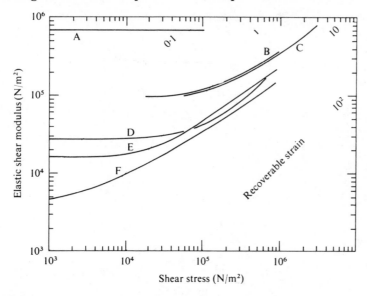

Figure 11.12 Typical shear elasticity data for six thermoplastics at atmospheric pressure. A. Nylon 66, 285°C ('Maranyl' A100). B. Nylon 11, 220°C. C. Acetal copolymer, 200°C ('Kematal' M90). D. Low-density polyethylene, 190°C ('Alkathene' WJG 11). E. Acrylic, 230°C ('Diakon' MG). F. Propylene/ethylene copolymer, 230°C ('Propathene GSE 108)

Assuming that the product is not subjected to external tensile forces at the die exit, it can be shown[22] that the relationship between swelling ratio in the radial direction B_{SR} resulting from shear flow through a long capillary die, and the recoverable shear strain γ_R corresponding to the shear stress at the wall at the die exit, takes the form shown in Figure 11.14. In order to accommodate swelling in the radial direction, longitudinal shrinkage occurs. For dies of uniform slot section, the swelling at the die exit depends not only on the deformation but also on the direction (normal to the extrusion direction) in which it is measured. It is found that the swelling ratio in the thickness direction B_{SH} is equal to the square of that in the transverse direction B_{ST}. The relationship between each of the two swelling ratios and recoverable shear strain are shown in Figure 11.14.

The time scale of deformation during a processing operation will determine whether the response to an applied stress will be predominantly viscous or elastic. To a first approximation the response will be largely elastic when the ratio of viscosity to elastic modulus called the 'natural time' or 'apparent Maxwell relaxation time' is less than the deformation time. For example, if a maximum shear rate of 10^5 s^{-1} during the moulding of an acrylic at 230°C

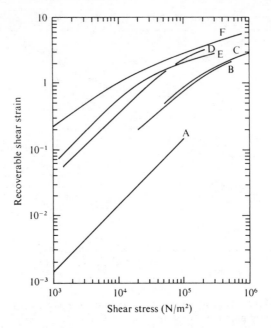

Figure 11.13 Curves of recoverable shear strain
vs. shear stress. A. Nylon 66, 285°C ('Maranyl'
A100). B. Nylon 11, 220°C. C. Acetal copolymer,
200°C ('Kematal' M90). D. Low-density polyethylene, 190°C ('Alkathene' WJG 11). E. Acrylic,
230°C ('Diakon' MG). F. Propylene/ethylene
copolymer, 230°C ('Propathene' GSE 108)

corresponds to an injection time of 2 s, the maximum stress (from Figure 11.5)
is 0·9 MN/m², at which the apparent shear viscosity is 9 Ns/m² and the shear
modulus is 0·21 MN/m² (Figure 11.12). The natural time 43×10^{-6} s is small
compared with the injection time, and hence the elastic component of the
deformation would be extremely small. For extrusion of a polypropylene
large-diameter pipe at 230°C at a shear rate of 10 s⁻¹, the shear stress is 27
kN/m², for which the natural time is about 0·45 s. Thus, if the melt takes 20 s
to pass through the die, the elastic component will still not dominate the
deformation, although the proportion will be much greater than that in the
injection moulding example. These two illustrations are typical of thermoplastics processing methods: the elastic component of deformation can
usually be neglected, relative to the viscous, in shear flows. (It should be borne
in mind however, that the effects of only small amounts of elastic deformation
can induce serious flow defects.)

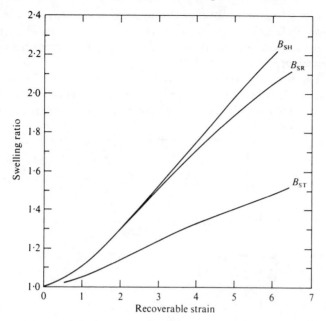

Figure 11.14 The relationship between swelling ratio and recoverable shear strain for long capillary and slot dies

11.2.2.2 *Tensile Elasticity*

At stresses up to 1 MN/m² it can be taken that the value of tensile modulus is equal to three times the value of shear modulus. The limiting tensile elastic strain is observed to be about two units in terms of true strain: this corresponds to a draw ratio of about 10:1.

When a thermoplastics melt flowing in a circular channel encounters an abrupt decrease in channel diameter, e.g. at the die entry, the material conforms to a natural angle of convergence for streamline flow. Superposed upon the shear flow, the convergence induces a tensile component of deformation which increases rapidly as the melt approaches the change in cross-section. In a long die this tensile component of flow will gradually relax as the material flows through the die; as no tensile deformation is developed in a fluid flowing within a die of uniform section, there will therefore be no recoverable strain at the die exit, and hence no swelling ratio corresponding to tensile deformation. For a very short die (sometimes described as a die of zero length), the tensile component of flow induced by convergence cannot relax before reaching the die exit. For a very short circular die the relationship between the tensile swelling ratio in the radial direction B_{ER} and the recoverable tensile strain (corresponding to the average tensile stress at the die exit) is shown in Figure 11.15. For flow through very short slot dies, the corresponding relationships for tensile swelling ratios in the thickness and transverse directions are also given in Figure 11.15.

The concept of natural time (viscosity/modulus) may be used to determine whether tensile deformation during a processing operation is likely to be predominantly elastic or viscous. For a long polypropylene parison at 230°C

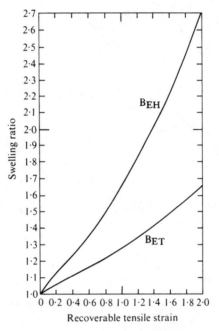

Figure 11.15 The relationship between swelling ratio and recoverable tensile strain for long capillary and slot dies

hanging for 5 s prior to inflation, the maximum tensile strain rate would be about 0·03 s^{-1}. The tensile viscosity is about 36 kNs/m^2 (Figure 11.11), and the tensile modulus 4·6 kN/m^2, giving a natural time of about 8 s, i.e. the parison sag will be largely elastic in nature.

Differences in the values of natural time (i.e. the ratio of viscosity to modulus) for tensile and shear stresses reflect differences between the viscosities. At stresses of the order of 1 kN/m^2 the ratio of tensile to shear natural times is approximately unity for most injection moulding and extrusion materials. At higher stresses the relative importance of elastic behaviour depends on the material. For example, for the inelastic nylon 66 at 285°C the natural time for tensile deformation is only twice the value for shear at 100 kN/m^2:

elasticity would play only a slightly more significant role in extensional flow than in simple shear flows of the same magnitude. With other materials, however, the tensile natural time can be as much as several orders of magnitude greater than the shear natural time at stresses in the range 100 to 1000 kN/m²: under these circumstances elasticity would play a much more significant role in extensional flow than in simple shear at the same stress.

11.2.3 Flow Defects

Flow defects, which are normally observed as visual imperfections in the product, can derive from sources such as poor product design, poor die design, inappropriate grade of material, inappropriate processing conditions and a difficult compromise imposed by economic and other considerations. These flow defects can vary in appearance from slight surface irregularities detectable as a loss of surface gloss, to gross irregularities affecting the body of an extrudate. Flow defects are sometimes accompanied by fluctuations in output rate, or in pressure drop. It should be remembered that flow defects are not always undesirable: defects are sometimes exploited, for example, in the production of matt surface finishes. There are at least six separate causes of these flow defects.

11.2.3.1 *Non-Laminar Flow*

If a thermoplastics melt flows through a capillary die in a steady stream-lined manner, adjacent parts of the melt round the circumference will recover, and swell evenly to produce an extrudate with a smooth surface. We have already mentioned that when a thermoplastics melt flowing in a circular channel encounters an abrupt decrease in channel diameter, the material conforms to a natural angle for streamline flow. This convergent flow pattern implies the presence of undesirable deadspots—regions in the die in which the material is held up with consequent change in thermal history—but, and perhaps more important, superposed upon the shear flow the convergent flow induces an extensional component which increases rapidly as the fluid approaches the change in cross-section. If the extensional stress reaches a critical value, the melt will rupture and 'fragments' of the melt will recover some of the extensional deformation; the frequency of this local extensional rupture will depend on the thermoplastic, the flow conditions, the relative change in cross-sectional area and on other factors. The effect is that the material at the die exit has a varying stress history, and therefore exhibits a varying recovery after extrusion, producing a distorted extrudate ranging in appearance from a matt finish to gross helical irregularities. This phenomenon is described in the literature as 'non-laminar flow', 'melt fracture' and 'elastic turbulence'.[15, 23] (It must be re-emphasized that the terms 'non-laminar' and 'turbulence' always correspond to low Reynolds numbers.)

The acceptable half-angle of entry, or maximum half-angle of free convergence α_0 into the narrow part of the die is approximately related to the shear and tensile viscosities[24] by the equation:

$$\alpha_0 = \tan^{-1}\sqrt{(2\eta/\lambda)} \qquad (11.12)$$

At low stresses, where $\lambda = 3\eta$, the half-angle of entry is about 40°. It is only at high stresses that the angle of entry depends on the nature of the material flowing through the die. The angle of entry will be large for materials which are Troutonian and relatively Newtonian, e.g. nylon, and for materials which are tension-thinning and strongly pseudo-plastic, e.g. polypropylene. The angle of entry will be much smaller for materials which are tension-stiffening and also strongly pseudo-plastic, e.g. low-density polyethylene.

11.2.3.2 *Sharkskin*

During flow through a die, the material adjacent to the die wall is almost stationary, but on leaving the die this material has to accelerate rapidly to the uniform velocity of the surface of the extrudate. This acceleration can produce a high local stress which, if too great, can cause rupture of the material at the surface of the extrudate, with a consequent deterioration in surface finish known as 'sharkskin'.[25] The appearance of this phenomenon can vary from lack of surface gloss to regularly spaced deep ridges perpendicular to the direction of extrusion. Sharkskin differs from non-laminar flow in that it is largely unaffected by die dimensions (e.g. die entry angle), it depends on linear velocity of extrusion rather than on extensional rate, and gross defects are perpendicular to the flow direction rather than helical or irregular. Sharkskin is least likely to be observed in material with a low molecular weight (i.e. low viscosity, giving a slow build-up of stress), and with a wide molecular weight distribution (i.e. a low elastic modulus, giving rapid stress relaxation) extruded at high temperatures and at low extrusion speeds. The use of die tip heating which reduces the viscosity at the surface of the melt, is effective in reducing sharkskin.

11.2.3.3 *Inhomogeneity*

Recovery of the elastic strain distribution in a previously deformed inhomogeneous material can cause lumpiness. The inhomogeneity can occur on a macroscopic scale (e.g. a tumble or extrusion blend of two or more materials) or on a molecular scale (e.g. one material with a wide molecular weight distribution). The nature of a particular process and application will decide on the type of material to choose. For injection moulding, a narrow molecular weight distribution will normally give a high gloss because the surface of the moulding conforms under pressure to the surface of the mould. If it is essential to achieve a high-gloss finish on an extrudate, then a narrow molecular weight distribution will be better at low output rates, and the maximum output rate will be dictated by the onset of 'sharkskin'.

11.2.3.4 *Volatiles*

Incorrect material handling prior to processing or incorrect processing conditions can introduce small quantities of materials which boil at processing temperatures. The volatiles often remain in solution under hydrostatic pressure and it is only when the pressure is reduced, e.g. when the material leaves the die, that bubbles may be formed in the body of the product, or that the bubbles may burst at the surface of the product, thereby impairing the surface finish.

Some materials are hygroscopic: precautions must be taken to ensure that these materials do not absorb moisture from the atmosphere before they are processed. Other materials degrade at very high temperatures to give volatile degradation products: the remedy here is to decrease the processing temperature somewhat.

11.2.3.5 *Shrinkage*

Thermoplastics contract on solidification from the melt and the contraction is greater for crystalline materials than for non-crystalline ones. Local variations in cooling will produce stresses which may cause surface distortions varying from a fine haze to gross defects. Sink marks, or surface depressions, usually occur above sections where there is local thickening; the core of hot material reduces the cooling rate of the surface and draws it inwards as contraction takes place. Voids are formed when the external surface of the product is rapidly cooled and becomes rigid enough to resist sinking; the contraction of the core then produces internal cavities. Voids assume particular importance in thick sections of transparent material. Ribs and bosses are the most common sources of a local increase in section thickness, and attention to careful detailed design can minimize or camouflage the shrinkage problems.

11.2.3.6 *Melt structure*

Interactions between high stresses, high pressures and low temperatures can give rise to the formation of pseudo-crystalline structures in the melt.[24] These result in such effects as anomalous changes in viscosity and unstable pulsating flows, giving an uneven output.

11.3 ANALYSIS OF FLOW IN SOME PROCESSING OPERATIONS

In thermoplastics processing equipment many kinds of complicated flow configurations exist. The following treatment is intended to provide an introduction to the analysis of flows and the exploitation of the properties of thermoplastic melts to three important production techniques: extrusion, extrusion blow moulding and injection moulding. The objective is to indicate that intellible solutions to design problems are available which provide a

Table 11.2. Some Important Rheological Equations

Class of flow	Shear	Pressure drop Extensional	Die entry	Swell ratio
(1) *Constant section die*				
Circular: long	$2L\tau/R$	0	$\dfrac{4\sqrt{2}}{3(n+1)}\dot{\gamma}(\eta\lambda)^{1/2}$	$B_{SR}=\left[\tfrac{2}{3}\gamma_R\left(\left(1+\dfrac{1}{\gamma_R^{2}}\right)^{3/2}-\dfrac{1}{\gamma_R^{3}}\right)\right]^{1/2}$
Circular: zero length	0	0	$\dfrac{4\sqrt{2}}{3(n+1)}\dot{\gamma}(\eta\lambda)^{1/2}$	$B_{ER}=(\exp.\varepsilon_R)^{1/2}$
Slot: long	$2L\tau/H$	0	$\dfrac{4}{3(n+1)}\dot{\gamma}(\eta\lambda)^{1/2}$	$\left\{ B_{ST}=\left\{\tfrac{1}{2}\left[(1+\gamma_R^{2})^{1/2}+\dfrac{1}{\gamma_R}\ln\gamma_R+(1+\gamma_R^{2})^{1/2}\right]\right\}^{1/3}\;;\quad B_{SH}=B_{ST}^{2}\right.$
Slot: zero length	0	0	$\dfrac{4}{3(n+1)}\dot{\gamma}(\eta\lambda)^{1/2}$	$\left\{ B_{ET}=(\exp.\varepsilon_R)^{1/4}\;;\quad B_{EH}=B_{ET}^{2}\right.$
(2) *Tapered section die*				
Coni-cylindrical	$\dfrac{2\tau}{3n.\tan\theta}\left[1-\left(\dfrac{R_1}{R_0}\right)^{3n}\right]$	$\tfrac{4}{3}\lambda\gamma\tan\theta\left[1-\dfrac{R_1^{3}}{R_0^{3}}\right]$	$\dfrac{4\sqrt{2}}{3(n+1)}\dot{\gamma}_0(\eta\lambda)^{1/2}$	$\left\{ B_{SR}=\left[\tfrac{2}{3}\gamma_R\left(\left(1+\dfrac{1}{\gamma_R^{2}}\right)^{3/2}-\dfrac{11}{\gamma_R^{3}}\right)\right]^{1/2}\;;\quad B_{ER}=(\exp.\varepsilon_R)^{1/2}\right.$

$$\left(\dot{\hat{\varepsilon}}=\tfrac{1}{2}\left(\frac{3n+1}{n+1}\right)\gamma\tan\theta\right)\qquad (\hat{\sigma}=\tfrac{3}{8}(3n+1)P_0)$$

Annular with double convergence	$\dfrac{2\tau}{H_1(U-V)} \ln\left(\dfrac{1+UL}{1+VL}\right)$	$\tfrac{1}{2}\lambda\dot{\varepsilon}\left[1 - \dfrac{R_1 H_1^2}{R_0 H_0^2}\right]$	$\dfrac{4}{3(n+1)}\dot{\gamma}_0(\eta\lambda)^{1/2}$	$B_{ST} = \left\{\tfrac{1}{2}\left[(1+\gamma_R^2)^{1/2} + \dfrac{1}{\gamma_R^2}\ln\{\gamma_R + (1+\gamma_R^2)^{1/2}\}\right]\right\}^{1/3}$
				$B_{SH} = B_{ST}$
Wedge	$\dfrac{\tau}{2n\cdot\tan\theta}\left[1 - \left(\dfrac{H_1}{H_0}\right)^{2n}\right]$	$\tfrac{1}{2}\sigma_{av}\left[1 - \dfrac{H_1^2}{H_0^2}\right]$	$\dfrac{4}{3(n+1)}\dot{\gamma}(\eta\lambda)^{1/2}$	$B_{ET} = (\exp.\varepsilon_R)^{1/4}$
		$(\hat{\dot{\varepsilon}} = \tfrac{1}{3}\gamma\tan\theta)$		$B_{EH} = B_{ET}^2$
(3) Spreading disc flow (Circular disc, centre gate)				
Isothermal	$\dfrac{2CQ^n R^{1-n}}{(1-n)x^{1+2n}}$	$\dfrac{\lambda Q}{4\pi x R^2}$		
Non-isothermal	$\dfrac{2CQ^n R^{1-n}}{(1-n)(xZ)^{1+2n}}$	$\dfrac{\lambda Q}{4\pi x R^2 Z}$		

Note: $U = (\tan\alpha.\sec\beta)/2H_1$; $V = n\left(\dfrac{\tan\beta}{R_1} + 2U\right)$; $Z = 1 - 2Y(A/Qx^2)^{1/3}$.

tractable basis for the optimization of a process. The text is mainly limited to a discussion of principles. The more important equations, including some which are not mentioned in the text, are summarized in Table 11.2.

11.3.1 Extrusion

Analysis of extrusion dies has centred on two extreme cases represented by circular and slot cross-section. It will be appreciated that an annular gap may be treated as a slot die, provided that the die gap to circumference ratio is small, other cross-sectional shapes being intermediate cases.

The simplest die is of uniform circular cross-section throughout its length. Given the shear rate, the shear stress can be determined (e.g. from Figure 11.5), and hence the shear pressure drop can be calculated for a given volumetric flow rate. No extensional deformation is developed in a fluid flowing within a die of uniform section, and hence the pressure drop within the die resulting from extensional flow is zero. Estimation of the extensional component of flow resulting from convergence at the die entry involves an iterative procedure: the average tensile stress at the die entry depends on the power-law index and on the die entry pressure drop; in turn the die entry pressure drop depends on the shear rate and the apparent shear viscosity at the die entry, and on the tensile viscosity corresponding to the average tensile stress at the die entry. The relevant equations are summarized in Table 11.2. The tedium of the iterative calculations necessary in order to establish the appropriate value of tensile viscosity (and hence to determine the die entry pressure drop) may be reduced by the use of a computer. Some refinements can be made to this basic set of calculations, to allow for the effects on pressure drop of increases in temperature and hydrostatic pressure.[26]

Although many sprues and runners in injection moulding machine nozzles are of constant cross-section, and pressure drops may be calculated in the manner described above, extruder dies are more frequently of tapered section (with or without a parallel section (land) at the die exit) because greater throughputs are normally required for economic production than can be delivered through dies of constant cross-section without incurring serious flow defects such as non-laminar flow.

There are three basic forms of tapered dies: coni-cylindrical (circular cross-section), wedge (slot cross-section) and annular with double convergence. The purpose of the taper is to eliminate dead spots and to reduce the value of extensional stress in what would otherwise be an abrupt change in cross-section. For efficient working, the angle of the taper should be much less than the maximum angle of free convergence calculated from equation (11.12): since the extensional strain rate is directly proportional to the tangent of the angle of free convergence, halving the natural angle of free convergence will produce only a modest decrease in extensional rate. Grades of low-density

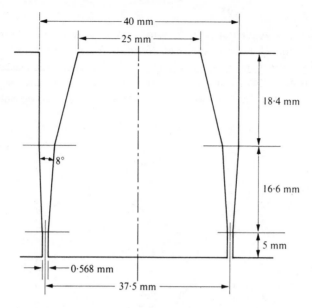

Figure 11.16   Principal dimensions (not to scale) of the die
discussed in section 11.3.1

polyethylene for making tubular film have a natural angle of free convergence
of less than 10°: dies with a taper angle of only $\frac{1}{2}$° are used in this process. By
comparison polypropylene has a very large natural angle of convergence,
and even modestly tapered dies generally improve performance. Equations
for predicting pressure drops in tapered dies have been published, and are
summarized in Table 11.2.

There are many reasons why practical die design procedures are seldom
made in exactly the straightforward manner described above. It is usual to
specify product dimensions and output rate. If the output rate is specified in
terms of extrudate velocity (because of cooling restrictions), then procedures
for calculating die exit dimensions will involve iterations to determine compatible values of swelling ratio and shear rate at the die wall. Should it prove
necessary to use a tapered die to achieve the required output rate, then the
angle of convergence must be chosen such that the extensional strain rate does
not exceed the critical value for non-laminar flow measured by rheometry.
A small angle of convergence may produce too large a pressure drop in a long
taper, and it may then be necessary to devise a multi-stage die in which there
is a progressive increase in taper angle in successive stages away from the
die exit.

Example

A tube of outside diameter 50 mm, wall thickness 1 mm, is to be extruded at 170°C and at a linear speed of 26 mm/s from a low density polyethylene for which data are presented in Figure 11.17. The die is to be used in an extruder, which imposes the following limitations on design: the die length should be 40 mm, and the die must fit an annular gap in the head of outside diameter

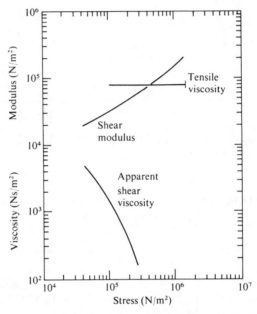

Figure 11.17 Typical flow data for a blow moulding grade of low-density polyethylene ('Alkathene' XHB 48 at 170°C, atmospheric pressure)

40 mm, internal diameter 25 mm. If the die land is 5 mm long, and not more than two tapers are to be used, recommend appropriate die dimensions and estimate the overall pressure drop.

Calculation of the die exit dimensions involves an iterative procedure in which values of die gap and die exit velocity are adjusted to be compatible with the associated swelling ratios. Assuming that the swelling of material at the die exit results entirely from simply shear recovery and that to a first approximation the annular gap may be treated as a simple slot of length = circumference, T, and of die gap H, the shear rate $\dot{\gamma}$ at any point on the circumference adjacent to the die wall resulting from a volumetric flow rate Q is given by

$$\dot{\gamma} = 6Q/TH^2$$

The average linear velocity, v, of the molten material in the die at the exit is given by

$$v = Q/TH$$

Hence

$$\dot{\gamma} = 6v/H$$

The calculations may be started by (erroneously) assuming unit swelling ratio, i.e. no swelling at all; on this basis the die exit velocity $v = 26 \times 10^{-3}$ m/s, and the die gap $H = 1 \times 10^{-3}$ m.

$$\dot{\gamma} = 6v/H = 6 \times 26 \times 10^{-3}/1 \times 10^{-3} = 156 \text{ s}^{-1}$$

The corresponding stress $\tau = 1{\cdot}32 \times 10^5$ N/m^2 and recoverable shear strain $\gamma_R = 3{\cdot}4$ (Figure 11.17), and hence from Figure 11.13 the calculated thickness swelling ratio $B_H = 1{\cdot}62$ and the transverse swelling ratio $B_T = 1{\cdot}27$.

The procedure now is to adjust values of die gap and die exit velocity. Thus, for the second attempt, the original die gap is divided by the new swelling ratio 1·62, and the original die exit velocity is multiplied by the product of the swelling ratios (to maintain constant volume). Thus

$$H' = 1 \times 10^{-3}/1{\cdot}62 = 0{\cdot}618 \times 10^{-3} \text{ m}$$

$$v' = 26 \times 10^{-3} \times 1{\cdot}62 \times 1{\cdot}27 = 53{\cdot}5 \times 10^{-3} \text{ m/s}$$

$$\dot{\gamma}' = 6 \times 53{\cdot}5 \times 10^{-3}/0{\cdot}618 \times 10^{-3} = 518 \text{ s}^{-1}$$

whence $\tau' = 2 \times 10^5$ N/m^2 and $\gamma_R' = 4{\cdot}05$ (Figure 11.17) and $B_H = 1{\cdot}76$, $B_T' = 1{\cdot}33$ (Figure 11.13).

This procedure is repeated until the agreement between successive calculations of swelling ratios is satisfactory. For the third attempt

$$H'' = 1 \times 10^{-3}/1{\cdot}76 = 0{\cdot}568 \times 10^{-3} \text{ m}$$

$$v'' = 26 \times 10^{-3} \times 1{\cdot}76 \times 1{\cdot}33 = 60{\cdot}8 \times 10^{-3} \text{ m/s}$$

$$\dot{\gamma}'' = 6 \times 60{\cdot}8 \times 10^{-3}/0{\cdot}568 \times 10^{-3} = 643 \text{ s}^{-1}$$

whence $\tau'' = 2{\cdot}1 \times 10^5$ N/m^2 and $\gamma_R'' = 4{\cdot}1$ (Figure 11.17) and $B_H'' = 1{\cdot}77$, $B_T = 1{\cdot}33$ (Figure 11.14), which represents adequate agreement. Thus the die gap is 0·568 mm, and the average diameter is $50/1{\cdot}33 = 37{\cdot}5$ mm.

Because the shear rate at the die exit, 643 s^{-1}, is much greater than the shear rate for the onset of non-laminar flow (about 150 s^{-1}, Figure 11.17), it will be necessary to use a tapered die. To avoid turbulence at the exit of the converging section of the die, it will be necessary to ensure that the tensile rate does not exceed about 18 s^{-1} (Figure 11.17). Treating the converging section as a simple wedge, the upper limit to the half angle of convergence, α, is given by

$$\alpha = \tan^{-1}(3\dot{\varepsilon}/\dot{\gamma}) = \tan^{-1}(3 \times 15/643) = 4°$$

Thus the full angle of convergence must not exceed 8°.

The length of the 8° taper section is determined by the shear rate at the entry of that section which should not exceed the critical rate for the onset of non-laminar flow, 150 s^{-1}. The die gaps at the entry and exit of the taper are related to the volumetric flow rate, which is in turn related to the shear rate. Thus, at the exit of the 8° taper,

$$Q = \dot{\gamma}TH^2/6 = 24\cdot5 \times 10^{-6} \text{ m}^3/\text{s}$$

Hence the die gap at the entry to the 8° taper is given by

$$H^2 = 6Q/\dot{\gamma}T = 8\cdot32 \times 10^{-6} \text{ m}^2$$
$$\therefore \quad H = 2\cdot89 \times 10^{-3} \text{ m}$$

Thus the taper length, L, is given by

$$L = \frac{H_0 - H_1}{2\tan\alpha} = 16\cdot6 \times 10^{-3} \text{ m}$$

The combined length of the die land and of the 8° taper is therefore 21·6 mm, leaving a length of 18·4 mm to be opened up to a die entry gap of 7·5 mm at the die head. This third section will act rather like a reservoir, and although it would be possible to consider it as an annular gap with double convergence (using the equations in Table 11.2), an adequate approximate procedure is to calculate the pressure drop in this section as if it were equivalent to the die entry pressure drop for the 8° taper. On this basis it is now possible to calculate the overall pressure drop in the die in two stages: (1) shear pressure drop in the die land, and (2) shear, extensional and die entry pressure drops in the 8° taper.

(1) Pressure drop in die land:

$$P_{s1} = 2L\tau/H$$

$L = $ land length $= 5 \times 10^{-3}$ m

$\tau = $ shear stress at exit $= 2\cdot1 \times 10^5$ N/m^2 at 643 s^{-1} (Figure 11.17)

$H = $ die gap $= 0\cdot568 \times 10^{-3}$ m

$\therefore \quad P_{s1} = 3\cdot7$ MN/m^2

(2) Pressure drop in 8° taper:

$$P_{s2} = \frac{\tau}{2n \tan \alpha} \left[1 - \left(\frac{H_1}{H_0} \right)^{2n} \right]$$

τ = shear stress at exit = 2.1×10^5 N/m² at 643 s⁻¹

$n = 0.3$ at 643 s⁻¹ (estimated from Figure 11.17, using equation (11.11))

α = half angle of taper = 4°, $\tan \alpha = 0.07$

H_0 = entry die gap = 2.89×10^{-3} m

H_1 = exit die gap = 0.568×10^{-3} m

$\therefore$ $P_{s2} = \underline{3.1 \text{ MN/m}^2}$

$$P_E = \tfrac{1}{2}\sigma_{av} \left[1 - \left(\frac{H_1}{H_0} \right)^2 \right]$$

σ_{av} = tensile stress at exit = 1.45×10^6 N/m² at 18 s⁻¹ (Figure 11.17)

$\therefore$ $P_E = \underline{0.7 \text{ MN/m}^2}$

$$P_0 = \frac{4\dot{\gamma}}{3(n+1)} (\eta \lambda)^{1/2}$$

$\dot{\gamma} = 150$ s⁻¹

$\eta = 9 \times 10^2$ Ns/m² at 150 s⁻¹

$\lambda = 8 \times 10^4$ Ns/m²

$\therefore$ $P_0 = \underline{1.3 \text{ MN/m}^2}$

The overall pressure drop in the die P is therefore

$$P = P_{s1} + P_{s2} + P_E + P_0 = \underline{9.3 \text{ MN/m}^2}$$

11.3.2 Extrusion Blow Moulding

In blow moulding it is necessary to consider not only the formation of the parison by extrusion, but also the deformation of the parison resulting from sagging and inflation. Most blow moulding machines extrude vertically downwards. Thus, under self-weight loading, the parison will increase in length, the strain having both elastic and viscous parts. If the time scale of the formation of the parison and delay before inflation is less than the natural time, then the deformation will be primarily elastic; if greater, then viscous deformation will assume major importance.

The simplest case would be to consider a suspended vertical softened thermoplastics tube initially of uniform section, of length L and of density ρ.

The stress at the top of the tube due to self-weight loading is given by

$$\sigma = L\rho g \tag{11.13}$$

If the thickness at the free end is H_0 and that at the suspended end at any time is H, then the maximum strain is given by

$$\varepsilon = \ln(H_0/H)$$

This strain results from an elastic component and a viscous component:

$$\varepsilon = \ln(H_0/H) = \frac{\sigma}{E} + \frac{\sigma t}{\lambda} \tag{11.14}$$

It is therefore possible, using these equations, to make a rough estimate of parison sag as a function of time.

In practice it may be desirable to take into account swelling and the finite time of extrusion, which can exert a major influence on parison sag, and detailed discussion is given in reference 26.

Parisons are frequently inflated to the final shape of the moulding by air introduced at a predetermined volume flow rate I, from which the tensile strain rate, $\dot{\varepsilon}$, at a radius, R, in the parison wall given by

$$\dot{\varepsilon} = \frac{I}{2\pi R^2 L} \tag{11.15}$$

It is most important that the inflation should be stable, i.e. that the resistance to deformation (the rate of change of internal pressure) should increase as the stress increases; in this way deformation will occur preferentially in the least deformed part of the parison. Certainly the tensile modulus increases with stress, indeed, the lower the value of tensile elastic modulus, the more pronounced is the stress dependence, as shown in Figure 11.12. The value of natural time for the material during the inflation stage should be large: thus for a low value of modulus at low stresses the viscosity should be high, so that the material will respond elastically to the high blowing pressure.

Provided the yield stress of the melt is not exceeded, the faster the inflation rate the more stable the deformation, and for equal stability the inflation time for mouldings of different sizes must be kept constant. It can be shown that for practical purposes the criterion for qualitative stability during inflation can be satisfied by the expression

$$\frac{1}{t'} < \frac{4I}{3\pi R^2 L} \tag{11.16}$$

where $t' = $ natural time; $R = $ radius of parison; $L = $ length of parison.

Thus, given the inflation rate, it is possible to calculate the tensile strain rate and hence the tensile stress. (If this value of tensile stress is greater than the tensile strength of the melt, the inflation rate will have to be reduced.) On this basis the natural time for the process, t', can be calculated:

$$t' = 8\varepsilon'/3 \tag{11.17}$$

Values of tensile viscosity λ and tensile modulus E corresponding to the prevailing tensile stress will indicate the natural time for the molten material, t'':

$$t'' = \lambda/E \tag{11.18}$$

If $t''/t' > 1$, then the parison inflation will be stable and satisfactory. If $t''/t' < 1$ the parison inflation will be unstable: it will then be necessary to increase the inflation rate. If $t''/t' < 1$, and an increase in inflation rate induces a stress greater than that which the material can withstand, then a material with a higher viscosity should be used. It follows that a good blow moulding polymer represents a compromise between conflicting requirements. To minimize sharkskin at high extrusion rate, the material should have a low elastic modulus and a low viscosity; for stable inflation the material should offer a low value of modulus and a high value of viscosity; to minimize parison sag at low stresses the material should have a high tensile modulus and a high tensile viscosity.

11.3.3 Injection Moulding

Developments based on the rheology of polymer melts and the principles of heat transfer have led to methods of predicting flow in injection moulding machine nozzles, in runners and into centre-gated square, rectangular and circular flat cavities.

The nozzle, screw and runner system for delivering the melt from the barrel to the cavity may be regarded as a series of dies of constant, diverging or converging sections.[28] The total pressure drop through such a delivery channel may be regarded as the sum of the die entry, shear and extensional components of pressure drop for each section, using the methods discussed in section 11.3.1. Appropriate corrections can be made, if necessary, for temperature and pressure changes.

On entering a cavity of uniform thickness from a central sprue, a melt front expands as a spreading disc.[29] For isothermal flow, the shear component of pressure drop at the instant of filling a circular cavity of radius R and uniform thickness x is given approximately by[29]

$$P_s = \frac{2CQ^n R^{1-n}}{(1-n)x^{1+2n}} \tag{11.19}$$

In practice the cavity is always cooled (to increase production rate), and allowance must therefore be made for the cooling and solidification of the melt on the cold cavity walls during the cavity filling operation. Experience shows that two assumptions can be made which greatly simplify calculations for non-isothermal flow: (i) at the instant the melt front reaches the cavity extremities, the layer of material frozen-off on the walls is everywhere uniform in thickness, and (ii) the thickness of material frozen-off is proportional to the cube root of the filling time, i.e.

$$\Delta x = Y(Ax/Q)^{1/3} \tag{11.20}$$

where A = surface area of cavity. The freeze-off 'constant' Y depends on the thermal diffusivity of the melt and on the dimensionless temperature parameter $(T_0 - \theta)/(T - \theta)$, where T_0 is the solidification temperature for the material, T is the melt temperature at the time of entering the cavity, and θ is the mould surface temperature.

Calculations of the shear and extrusional components of pressure drop for non-isothermal flow involve only the material characteristics C, n and Y; the cavity parameters R, x and A, and the injection rate Q. Optimization in the choice of injection rate to minimize cavity pressure gradients results in the lowest possible frozen-in stresses in the moulding.

It can be shown[30] that the minimum clamping force F during injection into a circular cavity depends only on pressure drop resulting in shear flow:

$$F = P_S \pi R^2 \left(\frac{1 - n}{3 - n} \right) \tag{11.21}$$

Similar analyses can be made of spreading disc flow into rectangular cavities of uniform thickness. For a moulded product of given design, analyses of these kinds help the designer to specify three injection moulding machine limitations which can assume critical importance during the injection phase of the moulding operation, i.e. maximum injection pressure, maximum injection rate and maximum clamping force. The maximum shot size can readily be calculated from the dimensions of the product. Once part thickness has been determined by stiffness or other mechanical requirements, the principles outlined above can be used to decide whether a given machine can produce the article, or what machine specifications would be needed.

11.4 CONCLUSIONS

This chapter has reviewed the fundamental concepts underlying the behaviour of thermoplastics melts, and has discussed the principles of analysis relevant to the design of the shaping of materials during processing. The three examples, extruder dies, parison performance and injection mould filling, are representative of a wide variety of processing situations which embrace wire-covering, tubular film production, extrusion coating, sandwich moulding and fibre spinning.

For the processor this analytical approach offers three points of direct interest. It defines scientifically the knowledge which he has already acquired by experience, thereby providing the opportunity to replace processing 'magic' by objectivity. The establishment of mathematical models of processing operations provides the necessary starting point for computer control, with the possibility of reducing processing costs in the long term. Finally, this approach provides the basis for scaling-up processes and predicting performance beyond the range of current empirical knowledge.

11.5 REFERENCES

1. H. J. Sharp, 'The need for an integrated approach to designing for plastics', Plastics Institute Conference, Cranfield, 4–6 January 1971.
2. E. G. Fisher, *Extrusion of Plastics*, Iliffe, 1964.
3. G. Schenkel, *Plastics Extrusion Technology*, Iliffe, 1966.
4. E. R. Martin, *Injection Moulding of Plastics*, Iliffe, 1964.
5. J. Bown and J. D. Robinson, *Injection and Transfer Moulding and Mould Design*, Business Books, 1970.
6. R. G. W. Pye, *Injection Mould Design*, Iliffe, 1968.
7. A. B. Glanville and E. N. Denton, *Injection Mould Design Fundamentals*, Vols. 1 and 2, The Machinery Publishing Co. Ltd., 1963.
8. E. G. Fisher and E. D. Chard, *Blow Moulding of Plastics*, Iliffe, 1971.
9. A. Thiel, *Principles of Vacuum Forming*, Iliffe, 1965.
10. J. Czerski, 'Injection-moulded foams', *Plastics and Polymers*, **39**, 406–411 (1971).
11. D. F. Oxley and D. J. H. Sandiford, 'Sandwich moulding', *Plastics and Polymers*, **39**, 288–292 (1971).
12. J. B. Borthwick, 'Extrusion of expanded materials', *Plastics and Polymers*, **39**, 415–419 (1971).
13. R. A. Elden and A. D. Swan, *Calendering of Plastics*, Iliffe, 1971.
14. A. Kobayashi, *Machining of Plastics*, McGraw-Hill, 1967.
15. J. A. Brydson, *Flow Properties of Polymer Melts*, Iliffe, 1970.
16. J. M. McKelvey, *Polymer Processing*, Wiley, 1962.
17. R. S. Lenk, *Plastics Rheology*, Maclaren, 1968.
18. J. R. A. Pearson, *Mechanical Principles of Polymer Melt Processing*, Pergamon, 1966.
19. J. J. Benbow, 'Modern techniques for measuring viscoelasticity in molten polymers', *Laboratory Practice*, 533 (June 1963).
20. ASTM D1238-70: *Measuring flow rates of thermoplastics by extrusion plastometer*.
21. F. N. Cogswell, 'Tensile deformations in molten polymers', *Rheol. Acta.*, **8**, 187–194 (1969).
22. F. N. Cogswell, 'Large elastic deformations in polymer melts', *Plastics and Polymers*, **38**, 391–394 (1970).

23. F. N. Cogswell and P. Lamb, 'The mechanism of melt distortion', *Trans. J. Plast. Inst.*, **35**, 809–813 (1967).
24. P. Lamb and F. N. Cogswell, 'Anomalies in the melt flow of polymers', International Plastics Congress at Amsterdam (1966), *Processing Polymer to Products*.
25. F. N. Cogswell, 'Converging flows of polymer melts in extrusion dies', *Poly. Engng. & Sci.*, **12**, 64–73 (1972).
26. F. N. Cogswell, 'The influence of pressure on the viscosity of polymer melts', *Plastics and Polymers*, **41**, 39–43 (1973).
27. F. N. Cogswell, P. C. Webb, J. C. Weeks, S. G. Maskell and P. D. R. Rice, 'The scientific design of fabrication processes: blow moulding', *Plastics and Polymers*, **39**, 340–350 (1971).
28. I. T. Barrie, 'An analysis of large-area moulding technology', *Plastics and Polymers*, **37**, 463–468 (1969).
29. I. T. Barrie, 'An application of rheology to the injection moulding of large-area articles', *Plastics and Polymers*, **38**, 47–51 (1970).
30. I. T. Barrie, 'Understanding how an injection mould fills', *S.P.E. Journal*, **27**, 64–69 (August 1971).

12

Principles for Using Design Data

by P. C. Powell

12.1 INTRODUCTION

Plastics are being used in many applications where substantial loads have to be carried and where economic considerations dictate the use of the minimum amount of material commensurate with satisfactory performance. There is mounting pressure to get the design 'right first time'; this is particularly important where expensive processing machinery costing more than £100,000 and involving tool costs in the range £20,000 to £40,000 is used, and in which the hourly use of raw material can exceed £100 in value. The designer normally seeks to ensure that a given article will not break, deflect or deform excessively, bearing in mind the penalties of overdesign.

Clearly, therefore, design must utilize a soundly based technology. Earlier chapters of this book have provided part of the background by describing the properties of thermoplastics relevant to design requirements. This chapter suggests ways of formulating the structural design problem to take the necessary factors, particularly time and temperature, into account so that the now familiar design data may be used to best advantage in avoiding potential causes of trouble and in comparing the behaviour of materials under conditions similar to those which obtain in service. This chapter also discusses currently available ways of assessing safety factors and of predicting long-term performance, bearing in mind the designer's need for tractable design methods which can accommodate some of the intricacies of real components.

Considerable quantities of design data are now becoming available both from the suppliers of plastics raw materials and from the trade press.[1-4] These design data certainly make a major contribution to the resolution of some of the critical parts of many design problems, and some examples will be given in section 12.5. It would be foolish, however, to claim that the data can completely resolve all problems. Not only are some well-defined problems extremely complicated, thereby defying rigorous or even approximate analysis, but it is as well to remember that some classes of articles can be subject to accidental damage and abuse, where loads may be unknown and where the route through the article by which the load is transferred from the point of application to the support may be far from obvious.

12.2 MECHANICAL DESIGN BRIEF

Many factors have to be taken into account in formulating the design brief for a load-bearing article.[5-11] Some of these factors are common to nearly all design problems, regardless of the material used to make the article. This category includes estimates of the total quantities involved, the desired rate of production and the maximum allowable manufacturing cost. Taken together with specified limits on the shape, size and weight of the article, information of this kind exerts a considerable influence on the choice of appropriate manufacturing method. It is worth mentioning that aesthetic, ergonomic and marketing considerations are also important, but these lie outside the scope of the present treatment.

Other factors, however, are more specific to the design of plastics articles. For functional or psychological reasons, limitations are frequently imposed on the amount of deflection or deformation in a structural member resulting from self-weight or externally applied loads. The reader will appreciate that it is necessary to specify not only the magnitude of the load but also whether it is a tensile, compressive or shear load. It is also necessary to specify or estimate the duration of the load. The simplest case is to assume that the load is applied and then maintained constant. However, if the load is applied periodically, estimates are required of the period of the load, the proportion of the cycle during which the load is applied and the total number of cycles which the article must withstand. Similarly, if the load is rapidly changing or is rapidly reversed in a periodic manner (e.g. fatigue loading), then it is necessary to establish the frequency of the stress change or reversal, and the value of the mean stress. The designer should ascertain whether proving or acceptance test conditions will be more severe than those which the article must withstand in service (e.g. a short-term test under high load or at a high temperature in place of the long term in service under a more modest load or at a lower temperature).

Superimposed on the above factors is the effect of the environment in which the article is to operate. A change in temperature can exert a profound influence on the properties of plastics. It is therefore prudent to ascertain not only the anticipated steady service temperature and duration, but also the likely (but realistic) maximum and minimum temperatures and durations which the article may encounter. It is also necessary to determine limitations imposed by exposure to weather, sunlight and other radiations, to humidity and water, to chemicals normally and occasionally in contact, and to erosive and abrasive media. It will be appreciated that some of these factors are exceedingly difficult to determine, particularly when a closely engineered thermoplastics article is to replace an overdesigned counterpart made from another material. It is hoped that the following examples will illustrate and clarify the principles stated above.

The designer is advised to avoid confusion between the required lifetime of an article and the duration of any loads during the lifetime. For a large outdoor sign fabricated from cast acrylic sheet and mounted in the vertical plane, the lifetime is normally specified as several decades, and the acrylic sheet readily meets the stringent weathering requirements over this period; for a well-supported sign the self-weight loading can normally be ignored, but the design must be capable of withstanding wind loading intermittently and for relatively short periods at a time. In contrast, for a horizontal roof-light the self-weight loading can be considerable, and this exerts its effect throughout the service lifetime; further intermittent loads can also result from occasional falls of snow.

In the design of a thermoplastics impeller the magnitude of the centrifugal forces causing the blades to elongate will depend on factors such as the diameter of the fan and on the speed of rotation; the effect of these forces will depend on the duration of rotation and on the temperature of the blades. If the impeller is connected to a car engine in order to direct cooling air on to the radiator, then it is necessary to assume for design purposes a meaningful 'average maximum' duration of journey at an 'average maximum' engine speed at an appropriate blade temperature. In contrast, if the impeller is bolted on to the drive shaft, the compressive forces holding the impeller in place will relax over the total estimated lifetime of the assembly in the car, which can be a period of many years.

The design of large vertical cylindrical storage tanks which are filled and maintained full at a given temperature is relatively straightforward. But if the duty for such a tank involved filling it with a hot liquid, which was subsequently allowed to cool, and if during this cooling period the tank were to be gradually emptied so that by the time the tank were empty the liquid was more or less at ambient temperature, the criteria on which to base the choice of wall thickness are very much more difficult to establish.

12.3 TWO POTENTIAL CAUSES OF TROUBLE

A study of earlier chapters of this book and of the design data suggests practical ways of avoiding potential causes of disappointing performance in service: the most important of these concern stress concentrations and processing conditions. The following typical illustrations apply to the complete range of failure modes including impact strength, creep rupture and dynamic fatigue.

It cannot be overemphasized that the designer should minimize stress concentrations wherever possible. An obvious source of these can occur at internal and external corners arising from changes in shape or in cross-section: the designer is strongly advised to use as generous a radius on corners as possible, and also to check that these generous radii have been incorporated in the manufacture of the mould or die. Sometimes, of course, a compromise is dictated by other considerations such as the undesirability of excessive sink marks opposite ribs on flat panels. It is worth remembering that screw threads with sharp thread forms can act as sources of severe stress concentration; the severity of this effect can be reduced by using rounded thread forms. A further source of stress concentration is the area on a moulding from which a gate, or even flash, has been clumsily removed: if this area is subjected to tensile stresses, the defects in surface finish can promote the likelihood of brittle failure in what may be an otherwise ductile material. Finally, when two parts are welded together, stress concentrations can be formed along the line of the weld by the surface irregularities.

There is a great economic temptation to process plastics at the lowest melt temperature: cycle times will be short and the article will be cheap to produce, but the impact strength may well be disappointing. Studies of the effect of changing the cylinder temperature on the impact strength at room temperature of a polypropylene show that for optimum impact performance the cylinder temperature should be in the range 260 to 290°C: some 90 to 120 degrees above the melting point. The cylinder temperature in this example represents a particular fabrication condition. For example, the effect of a long flow path in a thin-walled moulding is similar to that of moulding at a low cylinder temperature, in that the further the advancing melt front is from the gate, the cooler is the material; in the extreme case freezing-off could occur before the cavity was completely filled (n.b. section 11.3.3). Where thin-walled mouldings with long flow paths are to be produced, a high MFI ('easy flow') grade of material is generally preferred because such a material can be made to fill the mould rapidly (hence resulting in only a small drop in melt temperature), and with less strain frozen into the moulding the durability is likely to be better than if a lower MFI material were used.

12.4 COMPARISON OF THE BEHAVIOUR OF MATERIALS

Where chemical resistance and exposure requirements are not dominant features underlying the choice of material, a worst-case approach to the comparison of behaviour and to the prediction of performance splits into two parts: short-term (impact) and long-term behaviour.

12.4.1 Impact Data

From the impact data based on the Charpy type of test a broad pattern of behaviour emerges. Classification of materials into four categories ranging from brittle to tough[11] affords some general information on various materials at different temperatures as shown in Table 12.1. These data correlate with practical experience. Many grades of low-density polyethylene are exceedingly tough, even at low temperatures, and this has led to their use in the form of, for example, injection moulded dustbins. At the other extreme, general purpose polystyrene is not recommended for use in applications where impact blows are likely to occur.

Table 12.1. The Impact Strength of Thermoplastics

Material	Temperature °C							
	−20	−10	0	+10	+20	+30	+40	+50
Polystyrene	A	A	A	A	A	A	A	A
Polymethyl methacrylate	A	A	A	A	A	A	A	A
Glass-filled nylon (dry)	A	A	A	A	A	A	A	B
Methylpentene polymer	A	A	A	A	A	A	A	AB
Polypropylene	A	A	A	A	B	B	B	B
Craze-resistant acrylic	A	A	A	A	B	B	B	B
Polyethylene terephthalate	B	B	B	B	B	B	B	B
Polyacetal	B	B	B	B	B	B	C	C
Unplasticized PVC	B	B	C	C	C	C	D	D
CAB	B	B	B	C	C	C	C	C
Nylon (dry)	C	C	C	C	C	C	C	C
Polysulphone	C	C	C	C	C	C	C	C
High-density polyethylene	C	C	C	C	C	C	C	C
PPO	C	C	C	C	C	CD	D	D
Propylene-ethylene copolymers	B	B	B	C	D	D	D	D
ABS	B	D	D	CD	CD	CD	CD	D
Polycarbonate	C	C	C	C	D	D	D	D
Nylon (wet)	C	C	C	D	D	D	D	D
PTFE	BC	D	D	D	D	D	D	D
Low-density polyethylene	D	D	D	D	D	D	D	D

A: Brittle: specimens break even when unnotched.
B: (Notch brittle): specimens brittle when bluntly notched but do not break when unnotched.
C: (Notch brittle): specimens brittle when sharply notched.
D: Tough: specimens do not break even when sharply notched.

The designer has to choose materials from a wide range in order to overcome the difficulties imposed by severe combinations of values of temperature, of stress concentrations and of degree of orientation. The raw materials manufacturer offers materials within the same generic class with different impact properties depending, for example, on melt properties, molecular weight, copolymerization and additives such as plasticizers or glass fibres. Two practical points emerge. It is most unlikely that formulae will be developed in the near future which could be used to predict the performance of thermoplastics articles under impact conditions. Although some generalizations can be made, as illustrated in Table 12.1, it is recommended that the designer compare the impact behaviour of materials grade-by-grade, because generic groups such as 'nylon' or 'PVC' can cover an enormous range of behaviour.

12.4.2 Long-Term Data

In general terms, it is possible to compare the behaviour of materials in the long term using creep curves, creep rupture and dynamic fatigue curves.

From Figure 12.1 we conclude that at 20°C and 10 MN/m² the propylene homopolymer creeps less than the ethylene/propylene copolymer, and in turn nylon 66 at ambient humidity creeps less than polypropylene and so on. Curves of these kinds can be constructed from the basic creep data to conform with the temperatures and stresses prevailing in service. For example, Figure 12.2 compares an unplasticized PVC and a polypropylene at 60°C and at the more modest stress of 2 MN/m².

At short times under load the PVC creeps less, but after a few months the order of merit is reversed. There is no reason why comparisons of creep behaviour should be restricted just to the use of creep curves: isochronous, isometric and creep modulus curves may also be used. Figure 12.3 compares curves of tensile creep modulus vs. log time for an acetal copolymer, a dry nylon 66 and a polypropylene at 20°C and 1 % strain.

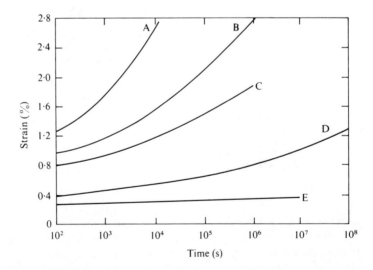

Figure 12.1 Creep in tension 20°C, 10 MN/m². A. Propylene/ethylene copolymer 903 kg/m³. B. Propylene homopolymer 909 kg/m³. C. Nylon 66 at ~65 r.h. D. Acetal copolymer at 65 r.h. E. 33% glass-filled nylon 66 at ~ 100 r.h

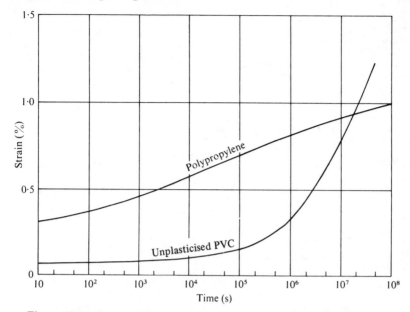

Figure 12.2 Comparison of tensile creep curves at 60°C and 2 MN/m²

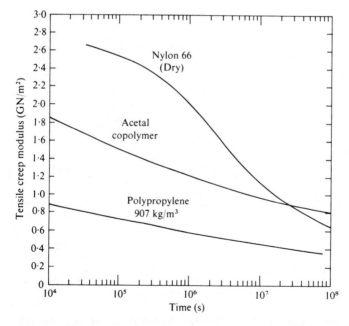

Figure 12.3 Tensile creep modulus vs. time curves at 20°C

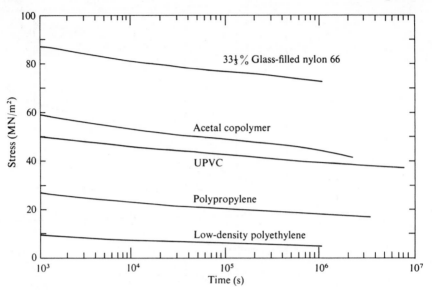

Figure 12.4   Long-term strength vs. time curves at 20°C

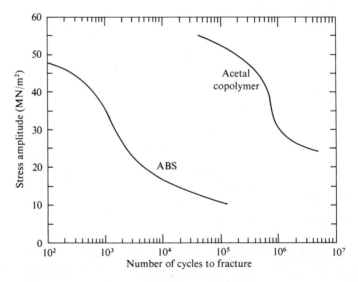

Figure 12.5   Dynamic fatigue characteristics at 20°C flexure at
0·5 Hz, zero mean stress square wave form

Similar comparisons of creep rupture data, and of fatigue data, can be made. Data at 20°C for certain grades of glass-filled nylon, calendered PVC sheet, acetal copolymer, polypropylene and low-density polyethylene are presented in Figure 12.4. Figure 12.5 presents data at 20°C for the fatigue behaviour of an ABS and an acetal copolymer under fully reversed square wave loading at a frequency of 0·5 Hz.

While making comparisons of this kind, it is necessary to bear in mind such points as the criteria of failure and values of safety factors, which may differ for different materials, and the effect of different environments on long-term behaviour.

12.5 PREDICTION OF LONG-TERM PERFORMANCE

The development of tractable analytical methods for predicting long-term load-bearing performance is inextricably linked with such factors as the economic incentive to use the minimum amount of material, the generation of design data, the development of manufacturing technology and experience of the performance of products already in service.

There has been something of an information explosion in the last decade concerning the provision of design data. Certainly an enormous amount of creep information has been published, much of it in line with BS 4618: 1970[12] and in parallel with the generation of these data there has been a gradual refinement of methods for predicting long-term deformation in a wide range of structural elements made from unfilled thermoplastics. In contrast, fewer data have been published concerning the long-term failure of unfilled materials and, indeed, recommendations for the presentation of long-term failure data are at a much earlier stage of preparation than their counterparts on creep and stress relaxation. This undoubtedly reflects difficulties such as the sensitivity of long-term failure to environmental and processing conditions, and the development of two rather different approaches to studies of failure, in which opportunities for regarding yield and crack propagation as complementary tools for the designer have not always been clearly presented. Meanwhile, commercial pressures have dictated an empirical approach to failure studies for particular classes of applications (e.g. hoop stresses in pipes) which provides the designer with specific and detailed information, the immediate usefulness of which more than makes up for its lack of generality.

12.5.1 Safety Factors

The traditional engineering approach has been to take a failure stress (e.g. yield or rupture) and divide it by a safety factor, the magnitude of which depends on a number of more or less related considerations, in order to obtain a design stress. This approach can be used for thermoplastics, always provided that the value of failure stress is appropriate to the expected conditions, particularly temperature and time under load. It is the basis for the design of pressure pipes for cold-water services to conform with British Standards; to withstand a given continuous internal pressure (head) for 50 years at 20°C, the safety factor for UPVC is about 2·1[13] and for high-density polyethylene about 1·3.[14] A similar approach can probably be used for more complicated stress systems, using the concept of equivalent stresses or some other yield criterion. For materials which fail, or which can be caused to fail, in the long term by crack propagation, the arguments for assessing an appropriate value of safety factor are much less well documented.

Whilst it is possible to design with an appropriate failure stress together with a safety factor as discussed above, there is growing support[15-19] for a maximum-strain approach to design problems. The choice of strain limit depends on the design problem, on service experience and on materials behaviour.

As far as the design problem is concerned, trouble may arise if a certain strain is exceeded because, for example, parts might not fit together properly, or excessive changes in shape may give rise to malfunctioning or be aesthetically or psychologically unacceptable (e.g. large deflections in beams and panels). Alternatively, parts designed to be transparent may craze at a strain below the fracture strain, thereby impairing the optical efficiency to an unacceptable extent.

Concerning the materials themselves, the design strain depends on whether the material is brittle (for which a low strain would be appropriate) or ductile (for which a higher strain would be appropriate); this in turn depends to some extent on whether loads are constant or have a dynamic component. Experience suggests that the tensile strain limits for well-designed injection moulded articles produced under appropriate controlled manufacturing conditions are:

Polypropylene	3%
Acetal copolymer	2%
Glass-filled nylon	1%

When welded polypropylene joints produced under normal fabrication conditions are stressed in tension across the weld line, stress concentrations introduced by the weld surfaces induce voiding at a nominal strain of about 1%. Although failure would not be expected to occur at strains of more than twice this value, 1% is normally taken as the design strain in welded polypropylene structures.[20] A detailed study of welded high-density polyethylene joints supports this argument.[21] Similarly, although cast acrylic sheet would not normally exhibit creep rupture in air at strains less than 3 %, it is the crazing at rather less than 1 % strain in the long term[22, 23] which imposes a limit on the working strain for design purposes.

The previous remarks apply to the design of articles operating in air only; if the environment is likely to induce stress-cracking, or stress-crazing, then lower values of design strain would probably be needed. A limited number of data support this view, and further comments will be made in section 12.5.8.

Having specified the maximum strain, together with estimates of duration of loading and the maximum service temperature, the design stress can be read directly from standard creep data. No further safety factor is required, concerning the behaviour of the material.

12.5.2 Uniaxial Deformation Under Constant Load

Thin-walled pipes, circular tanks, and gaskets providing a seal to bolted joints are examples of simple stress systems which induce uniaxial deformations of this kind. The normal design procedure is to couple a specific value of design stress, derived from the long-term test corresponding most closely to the anticipated service conditions, with a conventional stress or strain analysis of the assumed structural idealization. Uniaxial stress systems conform closely to the basic uniaxial tensile creep data, and it is possible to rely on the phenomenological relation between stress, strain, time and temperature.

This is the basis for estimating the maximum wall thickness of vertical, cylindrical, free-standing liquid storage tanks constructed by welding sheets of polypropylene.[20, 26] The design problem is concerned with resolving a hoop stress formula modified by a shape factor to take into account the assumed built-in end condition where the cylindrical wall meets the base of the tank.

$$\sigma_D \geqslant \frac{pR}{d} \hat{F}$$

where σ_D = design stress for polypropylene for a given strain ε, a lifetime t under constant load, at the maximum service temperature T; p = hydrostatic pressure for a liquid of density ρ at a height H above the base of the tank; R = radius of tank; d = thickness of tank wall; $\hat{F}$ = maximum value of shape factor, which depends on Poisson's ratio v, head of liquid, radius of tank and thickness of tank wall.

Since standard sheet sizes are used, the height and thickness of the tank are not continuous variables; given a certain capacity, the thickness may be reduced by increasing the radius, but limitations on radius are imposed by shortage of factory space or by transportation problems; and the height of the tank is normally chosen to be an integral number of sheet widths.

To simplify the choice of wall thickness the above equation may be re-arranged to give

$$\frac{\sigma_D}{\rho} \geqslant \frac{gHR}{d} \hat{F}$$

where g = acceleration due to gravity. The left-hand side of this equation may be plotted against liquid height, with sheet thickness as a parameter, as shown in Figure 12.6. The design strain for welded polypropylene is taken as 1% (see section 12.5.1); no further safety factor is required.

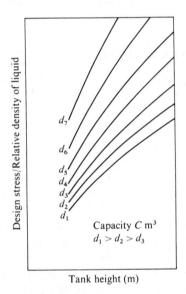

Figure 12.6 Design chart for a right cylindrical tank of capacity C and wall-thickness d_n

Theoretical predictions have been compared with experimental results obtained from a cylindrical tank 5·35 m high, 1·33 m radius and 6·35 mm thickness, which was deliberately underdesigned. Circumferential welds were reinforced with bands 300 mm wide and 6·35 mm thick. The maximum hoop strain was intermediate between the predicted values for uniform wall thicknesses of 6·35 mm and 12·7 mm (Figure 12.7). When the tank had reached a strain of double the imposed limit, the tank was emptied: the subsequent recovery behaviour was not as good as expected. Further work on the same tank has been reported: on refilling, the tank eventually burst at 2·4% strain.

Further theoretical work, using thinner walls in the upper parts of the tank, has been checked experimentally using an adequately designed tank 5·18 m

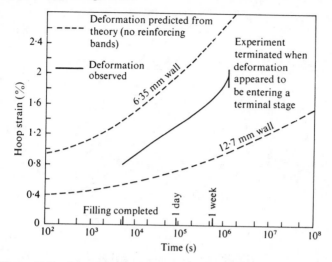

Figure 12.7 Actual deformation of experimental tank compared with calculated values. The calculations involved the assumption that the tank was filled instantaneously. The finite filling time leads to creep strains that are slightly lower, at short times, than those that would result from instantaneous filling. The discrepancy will be negligible after 5×10^4 seconds in this experiment

high. The tank was emptied after 17 months, and recovery behaviour was satisfactory. The conclusion was that the deformation in the tank was in good agreement with theoretical predictions, and that the design was as economical in the use of material as was feasible.

The previous example relied on the correct interpretation and use of creep data. A phenomenon closely related to creep is stress relaxation: the change in stress, which is time-dependent, resulting from an applied deformation. For most practical purposes stress relaxation may be adequately characterized by the isometric stress vs. log time curves obtained from creep tests.

Thus, if a sheet of acetal copolymer is bolted down at 20°C until the thickness has been reduced by 0·5% the stress in the sheet (across the thickness) after one year can be readily estimated. Referring to Figure 12.8, which presents isometric stress vs. log time data for acetal copolymer at 20°C, the stress corresponding to 0·5% strain after 1 year is about 4 MN/m². If the hub of an impeller were made from acetal copolymer and bolted down such that the acetal copolymer was compressed by 0·5% at 20°C, and if the relative expansion coefficient between the bolt material and the polyacetal were taken as 10^{-4} per °C, then at −30°C the plastic would theoretically be at zero strain. Clearly, the impeller should be compressed by more than 0·5% during assembly, if the fan is likely to be subjected to temperatures lower than −30°C.

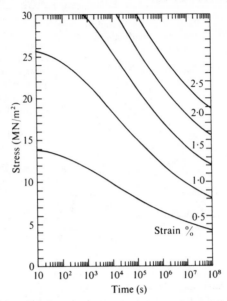

Figure 12.8 Isometric stress vs. time curves
20°C, ~65 r.h. Acetal copolymer

Waste-water pipes are often connected together by junction units injection moulded in polypropylene.[23a] The joint is watertight as the result of the hoop stress in the junction unit, but the hoop stress will relax, and it is necessary to guarantee that the joint remains watertight even after long periods of time, e.g. 20 years. A short-term water pressure test can be used to ascertain the suitability of the behaviour of the joint: if a test to atmospheric pressure (0·1 MN/m²) just produces a leak, it can be argued that this is a measure of the mating efficiency of the taper surfaces of the junction unit. The design problem then devolves on ensuring that the strain, to which the wall of the connecting unit is subjected when the pipe is forced in, is such that the relaxing hoop stress never falls below that corresponding to one atmosphere internal pressure.

For a wall thickness of 10 mm and a diameter of 150 mm, the critical hoop stress, σ_H, is given by

$$\sigma_H = \frac{0\cdot1 \times 10^6 \times 150 \times 10^{-3}}{2 \times 10 \times 10^{-3}} = 0\cdot75 \text{ MN/m}^2$$

Thus for a 20-year creep modulus of about 300 MN/m² at 20°C, the minimum hoop strain for an efficient seal is 0·25% for these dimensions. Even allowing for practical factors, this value would suggest that a thinner wall could be used rather than accept the economic penalties associated with an unnecessarily large built-in safety factor.

12.5.3 Flexural Deformation Under Constant Load

For flexural stress and deformation systems it is necessary to postulate not only a stress or strain analysis, but also a tractable (mathematical) relationship between stress and strain, in order to predict changes in shape. Many papers have discussed many different types of relationship,[19, 24-37] often with their advantages and limitations. Some of the proposals satisfy theoretical requirements with complicated analyses which may well prove intractable when dealing with all but the simplest structural idealizations. However, most designers can probably accept a modest measure of sacrifice in the accuracy of the design method, and the most useful and generally accepted design methods advocate the use of a time-dependent creep (or relaxation) modulus which is a straight-line approximation to the appropriate isochronous stress/strain curve, the approximation being based on a stated criterion such as a maximum strain, a maximum stress or even a maximum strain energy. (These methods represent a gross oversimplification of non-linear viscoelasticity justified by the realization that they work adequately in practice.) The immediate advantage of these simplified methods is that deflections and deformations in beams, plates, columns and other structural elements can then be calculated by using the appropriate value of tensile creep or relaxation modulus directly in the formula resulting from a classical elastic analysis of the structural idealization. This approach has been called 'pseudo-elastic design'.[24] Where a value of Poisson's Ratio is required, it is normally adequate to ignore time dependence and assume for sensibly isotropic structures a constant value for the given material, e.g. 0·35 for acrylic, UPVC and acetal copolymer, 0·4 for polypropylene and 0·45 for low-density polyethylene. The exact value is seldom important for isotropic thermoplastics.[35, 38]

In practice the strain involved in the flexure of beams and struts is normally small and a practical limit of $\frac{1}{2}\%$ has been suggested:[31] this can be readily checked when assessing the associated problem of outer fibre stresses. Thus strain, or its relaxed stress, is not normally an important parameter in calculating deflections in beams; the value of tensile creep modulus corresponding to $\frac{1}{2}\%$ strain, or the more frequently presented 1 % strain, can be used. In the deflection of plates, however, large stresses can be induced, and it is recommended that the estimation of suitable plate thickness to withstand a given load be based on an iterative procedure: first ensuring that the maximum design stress is not exceeded and then calculating the deflection based on the thickness dictated by the limit on design stress.

In its basic form pseudo-elastic design generally involves a worst-case approach. Loads are assumed constant for the service life of the article at a given (maximum) temperature, on the basis of which the value of the relatively low strain creep modulus may then be selected from creep data. The literature reports on the success of the method applied to simple and carefully controlled experimental conditions at about 20°C for deflections in beams,[27, 31, 32] buckling of beams[18, 31, 32] and deflections in plates.[25, 27] The basic design procedures for flexure are illustrated in the following numerical examples.

A cantilever beam, 6 mm wide, 15 mm deep and 120 mm long, made from cast acrylic sheet, is subjected to a load of 5 N at the free end. What is the deflection at the free end after one year at 20°C? The deflection at the free end after one year at 20°C?

The moment of inertia, I, of the beam is given by

$$I = \frac{6 \times 10^{-3} \times (15 \times 10^{-3})^3}{12} = 1\cdot7 \times 10^{-9} \text{ m}^4$$

The maximum tensile stress, $\hat{\sigma}$, in the outer fibres of the beam is given by

$$\hat{\sigma} = \frac{6PL}{bh^2} = \frac{6 \times 5 \times 120 \times 10^{-3}}{6 \times 10^{-3} \times (15 \times 10^{-3})^2} = 2\cdot67 \text{ MN/m}^2$$

After one year at 20°C this stress will result in a strain which is much less than 0·5%, for which the corresponding part of the isochronous stress vs. strain curve is sensibly linear. Hence, using the approach of Donald and Williams,[31] the one-year, 20°C tensile creep modulus at 0·5% will be appropriate for

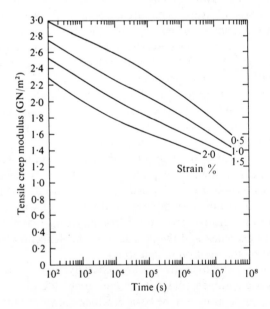

Figure 12.9 Tensile creep modulus vs. time curves 20°C ~65 r.h. Cast acrylic sheet

estimating the deflection in this beam. From Figure 12.9, the value is seen to be 1·54 GN/m². Hence the deflection $\hat{y}$ at the free end of the beam is given by

$$\hat{y} = \frac{PL^3}{3EI} = \frac{5 \times (120 \times 10^{-3})^3}{3 \times 1\cdot54 \times 10^9 \times 1\cdot7 \times 10^{-9}} = 1\cdot1\,\text{mm}$$

The next problem illustrates the way in which the dependence of the creep behaviour of nylon 66 on moisture content is taken into account. A cantilever beam in nylon 66 is 150 mm long, 6 mm wide and 12 mm deep. A load of 2·5 N is applied at the free end and held constant for one year at 20°C. By how much will the beam deflect if the nylon is in equilibrium with the atmosphere at (i) 0 r.h., and (ii) 65 r.h. ? The moment of inertia of the beam is given by

$$I = bh^3/12 = 6 \times 10^{-3} \times (12 \times 10^{-3})^3/12 = 864 \times 10^{-12}\,\text{m}^4$$

(i) From the tensile creep modulus/log time curve for dry nylon 66 at 20°C (Figure 12.3) the required value of creep modulus at 1 % strain after one year is about 860 MN/m². Hence the deflection at 0 r.h. is given by

$$\hat{y} = \frac{PL^3}{3EI} = \frac{2\cdot5 \times (150 \times 10^{-3})^3}{3 \times 860 \times 10^6 \times 864 \times 10^{-12}} = 3\cdot8\,\text{mm}$$

(ii) From isochronous data showing the effect of moisture content (Figure 12.10) the short-term creep modulus at 65 r.h. is approximately 38 % of the short-term creep modulus for dry nylon 66. Assuming that this behaviour is reflected in the long term, the creep modulus of nylon 66 at 1 % strain, 20°C, one year, 65 r.h. is about 330 MN/m². Hence

$$\hat{y} = \frac{2\cdot5 \times (150 \times 10^{-3})^3}{3 \times 330 \times 10^6 \times 864 \times 10^{-12}} = 10\,\text{mm}$$

If, however, the beam were made from $33\frac{1}{3}$ % glass-fibre-filled nylon 66 (rather than unfilled nylon 66), by how much would the beam deflect under the same load, if under water at 20°C?

Assuming equilibrium at 100 r.h., the modulus at this condition is required. Creep data for wet glass-filled nylon 66 (Figure 12.11) show that under a stress of 20 MN/m² the creep strain after one year at 20°C is 0·77 %. The isochronous stress vs. strain curve is linear up to at least 1 %, and hence the required value of modulus is 20 × 100/0·77 = 2600 MN/m². Hence

$$y = \frac{2\cdot5 \times (150 \times 10^{-3})^3}{3 \times 2600 \times 10^6 \times 864 \times 10^{-12}} = 1\cdot25\,\text{mm}$$

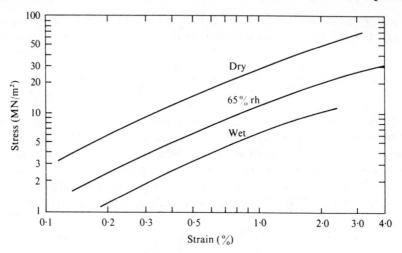

Figure 12.10 Isochronous stress vs. strain curves 20°C, 100s. Effect of moisture content on Nylon 66

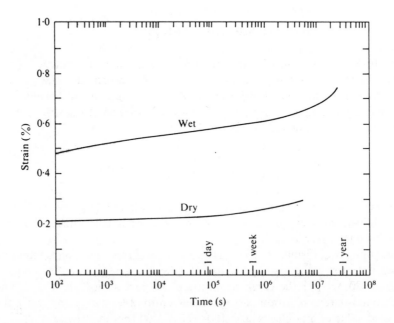

Figure 12.11 Creep in tension 20°C 20 MN/m². Comparison of wet and dry specimens. Glass-filled nylon 66

The maximum fibre stress in the beam is given by

$$\hat{\sigma} = \frac{Mh}{2I} = \frac{PLh}{2I} = \frac{2\cdot5 \times 150 \times 10^{-3} \times 12 \times 10^{-3}}{3 \times 864 \times 10^{-12}} = 2\cdot6 \ MN/m^2$$

This corresponds to a strain of a little over $0\cdot1\%$ in the glass-filled nylon.

In the prediction of buckling behaviour, the pseudo-elastic design approach uses a buckling load, or stress, formula in which the value of modulus is appropriate to the conditions of maximum time under load and maximum service temperature.

For example, in a certain type of crate[38] the vertical height of spaces in the side walls is about 75 mm, and the wall thickness of sides and ends about $2\cdot5$ mm, with substantial reinforcing ribs near the openings in the panels at least 9 mm thick. Crates of this type made from a propylene/ethylene copolymer failed during a test at 20°C after 1500 hours at a compressive stress of $2\cdot8$ MN/m². Failure in a stack of bottle crates usually results from buckling in the bottom crates. For simple rectangular struts, such as occur in crates, the critical stress at which buckling can occur is given by

$$\sigma_c = \frac{\pi^2 E}{6(L/h)^2}$$

Taking a value of 300 MN/m² (Figure 12.3) for the tensile creep modulus at 1% strain, 20°C and 1500 h, and allowing a 10% correction for the difference between tension and compression at 1% strain (Figure 12.12) the appropriate value of compressive creep modulus to use is about 330 MN/m². Hence, for a general wall thickness of $2\cdot5$ mm the buckling stress would be about $0\cdot6$ MN/m², but the local buckling stress in the reinforcing ribs would be at least $7\cdot85$ MN/m². Because the ribs constitute about one-quarter of the load-bearing cross-section, the overall critical stress would probably be about $2\cdot4$ MN/m². Practical trials support this calculation quite well. The limit of normal loading conditions in service would probably be realized by an average compressive stress of about $1\cdot6$ MN/m². Hence, the crate would operate in its service environment with a safety factor of about $1\cdot7$. Bearing in mind factors such as uneven load distribution and temperature variations, this value seems reasonable.

The following example compares the amount of material required when using two quite different materials (propylene homopolymer and a glass-filled nylon 66) in the design of a simply supported strut 200 mm long, which is to carry a load of 180 N at 20°C for 10 years. It is assumed that a hollow circular section is required, the wall thickness being arbitrarily fixed at one-eighth of the outside diameter. A load factor of 2 is used. The buckling load, P_c, for a

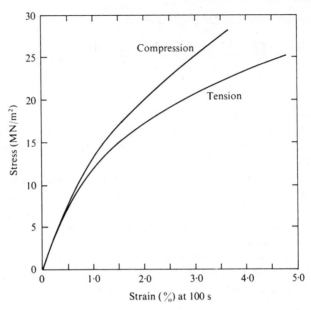

Figure 12.12   Isochronous stress vs. strain curves 20°C, 100s.
Polypropylene

strut depends both on the geometry of the strut and on the material from
which it is made:

$$P_c = \pi^2 \, EI/4L^2$$

The estimated value of creep modulus for the polypropylene is 320 MN/m²
and that for the glass-filled nylon 4200 MN/m². For propylene the required
moment of inertia is given by

$$I = \frac{4L^2 P}{\pi^2 E} = \frac{4 \times 0.04 \times 360}{\pi^2 \times 320 \times 10^6} = 1.82 \times 10^{-8} \, \text{m}^4$$

The moment of inertia of the hollow section may be expressed in terms of the
outside radius, R:

$$I = \frac{175}{1024} \times R^4$$

Hence

$$R^4 = \frac{1024 \times 1.82 \times 10^{-8}}{175} = 3.4 \times 10^{-8} \, \text{m}^4$$

$$R = 1.355 \times 10^{-2} \, \text{m} = 13.55 \, \text{mm}$$

For the glass-filled nylon, the required amount of inertia is $0 \cdot 1385 \times 10^{-8}$ m^4, corresponding to an outside radius of $7 \cdot 2$ mm.

In some applications the glass-filled nylon strut may be preferred, because it is just over half the diameter of the polypropylene one. However, it must be remembered that the raw material cost per unit volume of glass-filled nylon is more than four times that of polypropylene, and hence the cost of the raw material for the nylon strut will be higher than for the polypropylene one. The cross-sectional area of the polypropylene strut is about $63 \cdot 2 \times 10^{-6}$ m^2. In direct compression the load factor can be taken as unity and hence the direct compressive stress in the strut is $180 \, \text{N}/63 \cdot 2 \times 10^{-6}$ m$^2 = 2 \cdot 85$ MN/m^2. After ten years at 20°C this corresponds to about 1 % strain.

The previous examples on flexure have involved or assumed constant applied loads, for which creep data are directly relevant. However, in some design problems a flexural deformation is imposed, and it is then necessary to calculate the resultant thrust after a prescribed period. This is a stress relaxation problem which may be resolved by assuming (which it is nearly always safe to do) that tensile creep modulus data may be used in place of the formally required tensile relaxation modulus data.

For example, a spring moulded from acetal copolymer in a small mechanism takes the form of a curved beam built-in at one end. The beam is of uniform section 6 mm side, 3 mm thick, and its centre line is a quarter circle of radius 30 mm. If the spring operates at 20°C with an inward deflection of 3 mm at the free end, what is the force exerted by the spring after one year?

The deflection $\hat{y}$ at the free end of a curved beam of radius, R, subjected to a point load, P, at the free end is given by

$$\hat{y} = \frac{\pi}{4} \frac{PR^3}{EI}$$

where

$I = $ moment of inertia $= 13 \cdot 5 \times 10^{-12}$ m^4;

$E = $ tensile creep (or relaxation) modulus $= 900$ MN/m^2 at 1 % strain, 20°C,

one year (Figure 12.3);

$$P = \frac{4EI\hat{y}}{\pi R^3} = \frac{4 \times 900 \times 10^6 \times 13 \cdot 5 \times 10^{-12} \times 3 \times 10^{-3}}{\pi \times (30 \times 10^{-3})^3} = 1 \cdot 72 \text{ N.}$$

12.5.4 Behaviour at Temperatures Significantly Different from 20°C

Although long-term deformation at a given stress depends markedly on temperature, almost all the verifications of design procedures have been made at about 20°C. Creep data at temperatures above 20°C do not normally include thermal expansion effects and, for the most part, neither do the design procedures. For simple stress systems, such as cylindrical tanks and hoop stresses in pipes, even a considerable increase in temperature can be taken into account in a straightforward way.

For flexural systems, however, a more careful consideration may be required. Some structural elements need not be cause for concern in this respect, because the thermal expansion is effectively designed out, e.g. the simple cantilever. On the other hand, it is easy to envisage relatively unmovable boundary conditions which could impose severe difficulties: for example, long pipe runs with inadequate provision of expansion joints or loops, and glazing panels which have been fastened to frames without proper allowance for expansion. In these circumstances an increase in temperature induces compressive strains and the associated compressive stresses will relax with time.

Suppose, for example, that a load applied at midspan to a relatively deep encastré beam produces an outer-fibre strain of 0·4% as calculated by pseudo-elastic design using data for 60°C. If the system were set up at 20°C with fixed constraints, there would be an associated compressive strain of, say, 0·4% (for an acetal copolymer beam). The implication here is that the neutral axis would shift and this perhaps betrays the inadequacy of such a simple approach. On the other hand, no papers have been published which discuss the prediction of deformation in thermoplastic beams subjected to combined axial and transverse loads.

12.5.5 Deformation Under Periodic Loads

The discussion of the prediction of long-term deformation so far has assumed constant load conditions. In practice, however, some articles are subjected to periodic loading: where this condition can be guaranteed to obtain, significant reductions in raw material usage may be realized (compared with constant load conditions at the same stress) with the added attraction of a possible increase in production rate because less material has to be heated and then cooled.

Some creep data have already been published for step-function load/no-load cycles as discussed in Chapter 3, and ways of estimating data have been published[39, 42, 43] to cover some situations for which experimental data are not available. Uniaxial stress systems such as pipes and circular tanks conform closely to the experimental creep data under periodic load, and the prediction of the necessary component dimensions is relatively straightforward.

For example, a blow-moulded polypropylene container 120 mm o.d. with one hemispherical end is required to withstand an operating pressure of 0·6 MN/m² at 20°C. If the estimated service lifetime is one year, and the maximum allowable strain is 1·75%, what is the minimum wall thickness for

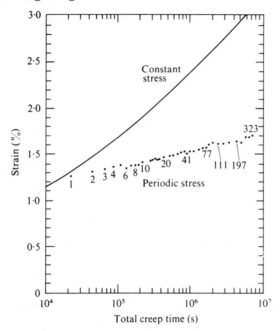

Figure 12.13 Creep in tension under periodic stress 10 MN/m² 20°C. Polypropylene density 0·907 kg/m³

satisfactory operation (i) under constant pressure conditions and (ii) under 6 hours per day at 0·6 MN/m² and 18 hours unpressurized?

(i) Under contant load conditions, the design stress for polypropylene at 20°C, 1·75% strain, one year is about 6 MN/m² (Figure 12.13). The minimum wall thickness under constant pressure conditions is therefore given by

$$t = \frac{pD}{2\sigma} = \frac{0·6 \times 10^6 \times 120 \times 10^{-3}}{2 \times 6 \times 10^6} = 6 \times 10^{-3} \text{ m } (0·24 \text{ in})$$

(ii) From creep data under periodic loading conditions, the strain after 365 cycles of 6 hours per day under a stress of 10 MN/m² is about 1·75% (Figure 12.14). The design stress therefore is 10 MN/m². Hence the minimum wall thickness under the specified periodic pressure conditions is given by

$$t = \frac{pD}{2\sigma} = \frac{0·6 \times 10^6 \times 120 \times 10^{-3}}{2 \times 10 \times 10^6} = 3·6 \times 10^{-3} \text{ m}$$

The economic advantages of taking periodic loading into account stem not only from a reduction of about 40% in material used per item, but also from a shorter production cycle.

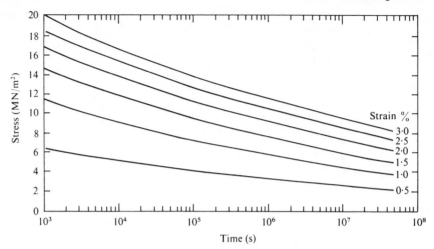

Figure 12.14 Isometric stress vs. time curves at 20°C. Propylene homopolymer 907 kg/m³

It is also possible to predict flexural deformations resulting from periodic loads using the pseudo-elastic design procedure, in which the value of design modulus derives essentially from low strain cross-plots of the corresponding uniaxial creep data under periodic loading.[43]

A polypropylene cantilever beam 100 mm long, of rectangular section 6 mm wide and 25 mm deep, carries a load of 62·5 N at the free end. What will be the maximum deflection after 10 days at 20°C under (i) constant load? (ii) periodic load for 6 h/day?

The moment of inertia $I = 6 \times 10^{-3} \times (25 \times 10^{-3})^3/12 = 7{\cdot}81 \times 10^{-9}$ m⁴

The maximum stress in the beam is given by

$$\hat{\sigma} = \frac{6 \times 62{\cdot}5 \times 100 \times 10^{-3}}{6 \times 10^{-3} \times (25 \times 10^{-3})^2} = 10 \text{ MN/m}^2$$

(i) The strain resulting from a constant stress of 10 MN/m² applied for 10 days at 20°C is 2·3% (Figure 12.14). This strain is much greater than the value recommended by Donald and Williams[31] for normal beam calculations, and hence the large strain creep modulus should be used:

$$E_c = \sigma_c/\varepsilon_c = 10 \times 10^6/2{\cdot}3 \times 10^{-2} = 435 \text{ MN/m}^2$$

whence

$$\hat{y}_c = \frac{62{\cdot}5 \times (100 \times 10^{-3})^3}{3 \times 425 \times 10^6 \times 7{\cdot}81 \times 10^{-9}} = 6{\cdot}1 \text{ mm}$$

(ii) At the end of the tenth loading cycle the strain resulting from 10 MN/m^2 applied for 6 h/day is $1 \cdot 4\%$ (Figure 12.13). The deflection calculation is treated as if it were a constant load problem in which the stress produces $1 \cdot 4\%$ strain after the required time period of 10 days, here 7 MN/m^2 (Figure 12.14). Hence the required value of modulus is

$$E_p = 7 \times 10^6/1 \cdot 4 \times 10^{-2} = 500 \text{ MN/m}^2$$

whence

$$y_p = \frac{62 \cdot 5 \times (100 \times 10^{-3})^3}{3 \times 500 \times 10^6 \times 7 \cdot 81 \times 10^{-9}} = 5 \cdot 3 \text{ mm}$$

12.5.6 Composite Materials

Both the linear elastic formulae and the design data must be appropriate to the design problem. The assumptions underlying the formulae are that materials are isotropic, uniform and linear elastic, that materials behave the same way in tension and in compression, and that deflections and strains are small. Some of these points have been mentioned in Chapter 3 and are discussed in more detail elsewhere.[35] There are, however, two further points which should be borne in mind.

The first point is that the pseudo-elastic design method takes no account of locked-in processing stresses; at present this topic is seldom discussed in terms appropriate to the prediction of performance and it is normally relegated to the province of 'field experience' and of prototype development exercises. The second point concerns the assumption of isotropy implicit in pseudo-elastic design. There are two particular areas of composite materials where the properties of structural elements can be particularly anisotropic: sandwich panels and articles made from fibre-filled thermoplastics.

Examples of sandwich panel contructions are the acrylic-capped ABS sheets used to make thermoformed articles with good weather resistance and a hard surface, and injection moulded sandwich structures in which the surrounding skin can be a solid thermoplastic and the core a foamed (or uniform, solid) material of the same or even a different thermoplastic. Methods for predicting deflections in such structures have been discussed in the literature, the normal assumption being that both the skin and the core may be regarded as sensibly isotropic.[37, 44, 45]

It is becoming increasingly clear that fibre-filled thermoplastics cannot be regarded as isotropic when processed into structural elements.[46] Upper and lower bounds for properties corresponding to along and across the direction of fibre orientation have been published,[47, 48] but tractable and widely used design methods have yet to be developed in which these materials can be utilized to best economic advantage. On the one hand it is difficult to isolate the really important aspects of the theory of the behaviour of anisotropic materials, and on the other hand to assess with confidence how anisotropic the properties are likely to be in the critical regions of an article produced by a given method under a given set of conditions.

12.5.7   The Effective Use of Shape

Deformations in beams and plates are inversely proportional to the product of modulus, a property of the material, and moment of inertia, a property of the shape used in design. All other things being equal, performance can be changed by varying either modulus, or moment of inertia, or both. Some shapes resist deformation (resulting from external loads, self-weight loads or stresses residual from processing) better than others, and the informed designer exploits shape to advantage to offset the rather low values of creep modulus which thermoplastics have compared with the values of modulus for most metals.

Even in the early days of bottle-crate design the importance of geometrical shape on stiffness was recognized. Hahmann et al.[49] demonstrated clearly that designs using a large amount of material were not necessarily the best, and pointed out that the important factor is the rational distribution of material. Morris and Whittal[50] demonstrated that small amounts of material judiciously placed can make an important difference to the stacking behaviour of milk crates injection moulded from high-density polyethylene: the addition of vertical ribs at corners reduced compressive creep by about 40%, and the removal of eight corner ribs weighing 170 g from a crate originally weighing 3·15 kg reduced the crushing strength by 25%.

Although beams of solid rectangular cross-section are suitable for many purposes, it is often preferable to use shapes such as hollow, channel, T and I sections, which are more efficient on a weight basis (because they use less material) and which require a shorter moulding cycle because of lower part thickness. The moments of inertia of these simple sections, and hence stresses and deflections, can be calculated from first principles, but some caution will be necessary where the use of very wide flanges is contemplated.[51]

Thick panels are expensive because they represent the inefficient use of large quantities of material and because the long heating and cooling times result in low production rates. Three devices are widely used to improve geometrical stiffness: ribbing, curvature and shaping. These devices increase tool costs, but in a long production run these may be more than offset by shorter moulding cycles and by the use of fewer raw materials. There are also some interesting new possibilities in recent innovations such as integral-skin, foamed-core mouldings.

The following example compares the salient features of two simply supported panels each 300 mm square. One is 2 mm thick, carrying ribs on a 20 mm square pitch parallel to the sides of the square; the ribs are 2 mm thick and stand 9 mm proud of the panel. A panel of uniform thickness made from the same material would have the same apparent flexural stiffness if it were 5·1 mm thick. However, the ribbed panel uses about 72 % as much material as the solid panel and could be produced more quickly: for polypropylene the cycle time of the ribbed panel could be about 60 % of that of the solid one. The actual break-even point on the cost of producing such an item, bearing in mind the increased tool costs for the ribbed panel, would depend markedly on the numbers involved. If a panel of the same apparent flexural stiffness were made from a glass-fibre filled nylon 66, for which the creep modulus was 15 times that of the polypropylene, then the thickness of a uniform panel would be about 2 mm. The cycle time would certainly be shorter than that of the polypropylene panel, but it is likely that the cost of the manufactured item would be greater than that of either the ribbed or the uniform polypropylene panel, largely as a result of the higher raw material cost of the glass-filled nylon. (It should be noted that this example relates to deflections resulting from a uniformly distributed load. Different types of loading conditions, e.g. the twisting of two parallel edges, could reverse the relative performance of the two panels.)

On a principle similar to that used in the ribbed panel, many decorative building panels are made from low relief shapings, where the design imparts stiffness to the panels by, effectively, a local increase in panel thickness, and this enables economies to be made in the choice of sheet thickness.

Ribbed panels may be unsuitable for some applications (i) because of sink marks on the flat skin associated with the underlying ribs, (ii) because of the possible difficulties of filling the mould cavity and subsequent difficulties of ejecting the moulding from the mould (even with tapered ribs), or (iii) because the performance of the panel in the optimum geometrical configuration still does not meet the design requirements.

Under these conditions it is worth considering the use of foamed material, with or without a solid outer skin. In structural applications foamed thermoplastics can offer a high stiffness-to-weight ratio and can afford a wide range of depths of section (for high moment of inertia and improved torsional stiffness). The integral-skin sandwich injection moulding process[44] has the further advantage that at the surface of the panel the material is unfoamed: this process therefore produces a density distribution which is particularly advantageous in flexure. Estimates of the likely behaviour of such a composite structure can be made, as described in section 12.5.

It is generally recognized that curved shapes can be stiffer in bending than flat shapes of the same weight. A square-section container to withstand a given pressure will usually be heavier than one of circular section and of the same volumetric capacity. Both single and double curvature are widely used to make more effective use of materials. A common example of single curvature as a structural element is the corrugated roofing panel, which is inherently much stiffer than if the same volume of material were used as a flat sheet. Some calculation can be made of the stiffness of corrugated panels under certain loading conditions. To improve further the stiffness, the corrugated panels are sometimes slightly curved along the length of the corrugations. Doubly-curved shells may take the form of spherical domes, or they may be anticlastic, or saddle-shaped, e.g. the hyperbolic paraboloids used in advanced architectural designs. Both types of double-curvature provide efficient structural shapes, but the saddle-shaped shells provide a higher buckling resistance than spherical domes of comparable curvature and thickness.[52]

12.5.8   Prediction of Long-Term Failure

Although methods for predicting long-term deformation are formalized in the pseudo-elastic design approach, procedures for predicting, and avoiding, long-term failure are less well developed.

Studies of ductile failure of thermoplastics under constant load[21, 53, 54] suggest an upper limit to the stresses which a material can withstand under given environmental conditions. As mentioned in section 12.5.1, the traditional approach for uniaxial stress systems is to divide the appropriate value of failure stress by a safety factor and use the resulting design stress in standard strength-of-materials formulae. This is the basis for calculating the minimum wall thickness for pressure pipe to conform with British Standards requirements,[12, 13] and a considerable body of practical experience has accumulated in this area, where the avoidance of rupture in the long term is of paramount importance.

It is interesting to note that when BS 3505 was introduced in 1962 the 20°C, 50-year design stress for UPVC pipe made to this standard was 7·85 MN/m². To conform with BS 3505: 1962 samples of UPVC pipe had to have a 50-year burst stress (estimated by extrapolation) of 20·6 MN/m² at 20°C. Thus, in 1962 the implied safety factor was about 2·63. In 1964 increasing and satisfactory experience led to the design stress being raised to 9·8 MN/m², thereby reducing the safety factor to about 2·1.

With the advance of both material and machinery technology it has been found that the estimated 50-year, 20°C burst stress could be well in excess of 20·6 MN/m², especially in the larger sizes of pipe. Because of this the 50-year burst-stress test requirement (BS 3505: 1968) was raised to 23 MN/m² for pipe up to 7 in diameter and to 26 MN/m² for pipe of 8 in diameter and above. The design stresses were also uprated to 11 and 12·3 MN/m² respectively. These design stresses correspond again to a safety factor of about 2·1. In practical terms, therefore, pipes designed to BS 3505: 1968 have thinner walls than those designed to the 1962 Standard. This fact alone makes UPVC pipe increasingly competitive on first cost with, for example, cast-iron pipe up to 8 in diameter for 500 ft head, and up to 12 in diameter at lower heads. In terms of laid cost the larger UPVC pipes can also be more economical.

Similar studies of high-density polyethylene pipes have been made. The calculation of the wall thickness required (52 mm) for a 1500 mm diameter pipe which has to withstand a head of sewage equivalent to an internal pressure of 0.35 MN/m^2 for 50 years at $20°C^{55}$ is based on the procedures laid down in BS 3284.[14]

Large-strain theory based on the concepts of equivalent stresses, or another yield criterion, can also be used to predict ductile failure: this is the basis of limit analysis for thermoplastics, and useful discussions of bending of beams and plates, and of the behaviour of rotating discs and thick-walled cylinders have been published.[28, 56] Thus, where it is anticipated that a material would fail in a ductile manner, proven design methods are available.

However, studies of long-term failure show that some materials under constant load fail at low strains by crack propagation. Other materials, which would normally be expected to fail in air in a ductile manner in the long term when under constant load, fail by crack propagation as the result of, for example, tests made in air under dynamic loading or in an active environment under constant (or dynamic) loading. Often crazing, or cracking (or both), precedes the mechanical failure. Under these circumstances the procedure for predicting performance is by no means unambiguous.

On the one hand it is possible to adopt a phenomenological approach: from experimental data[22, 53, 54] the value of stress defining low-strain failure after a given time at a given temperature, divided by a safety factor, can be used in the appropriate strength-of-materials formula. This has the merit of being a tractable approach.

An alternative approach is that of linear elastic fracture mechanics,[57-59] which is based on a detailed analysis of the stresses in the region of a defined flow or stress concentration such as a hole or a sharp crack. This approach can be applied to defects which are stressed in a variety of ways[60] and many workers have applied the principles of fracture mechanics to studies of crack propagation in structural idealizations, e.g. ultra-sharp notches, which are chosen for their experimental and analytical convenience rather than for their similarity to the shapes and sizes of real articles. For low-stress fractures a fracture-toughness (or stress-intensity) parameter for a given material under specified conditions can be measured, the value depending on most of the factors discussed in earlier chapters of this book, such as temperature, time (e.g. crack speed), the nature of the stress (e.g. constant loads or dynamic loads[61]) and the effect of any active environment.[62, 63] Thus, given an appropriate value of fracture-toughness parameter, it is in principle possible to calculate for a material prone to brittle cracks either the maximum load that can be withstood by the component for a given flaw size or, less commonly, for a given applied load the maximum value of flaw size that can be tolerated. A source of real difficulty is the transformation of the theory from the simple shapes from which values of fracture-toughness parameters are measured to the complicated shapes of commercially produced articles. The application of this technique to practical design problems normally relies on the judicous choice of a critical flaw size, and the current cautious suggested values result in design stresses which are disconcertingly low and which tend not to correlate too closely with practical service experience.

12.6 REFERENCES

1. R. M. Ogorkiewicz (Ed.), *Engineering Properties of Thermoplastics*, Wiley, 1970.
2. *Plastics Materials Guide*, Engineering Chemical & Marine Press, current edition.
3. *Design Engineering Plastics Handbook*, Morgan-Grampian (Publishers), 1971.
4. *Modern Plastics Encyclopaedia*, Modern Plastics, current edition.
5. R. S. Hagan and J. L. Isaacs, 'Characterization requirements for plastics in appliance applications', *Materials Research & Standards*, **10**, 9–14, 46, 48, 50 (1970).
6. *Plastics for the Design Engineer*, Plastics Institute, London, 1968.
7. M. M. Hall, 'An approach to material selection—engineering with plastics', *British Plastics*, **44**, 85–88 (1971).
8. J. H. Postans, 'Long-term failure and evaluation', Plastics Institute conference on *Service Failures in Thermoplastics*, London, December, 1969.
9. M. S. Madan and R. A. Letts, 'The design of air impellors in thermoplastics', *Trans. J. Plast. Inst.*, **33**, 113–118 (1965).
10. S. Joisten, U. Knipp, H. Schulze, A. Trauzold and O. Walter, 'Economic design of plastics mouldings', *Kunststoffe*, **61**, 325–331 (1971).
11. P. I. Vincent, *Impact Strength and Service Performance of Thermoplastics*, Plastics Institute, 1971.
12. BS 4618: 1970 *Recommendations for the Presentation of Plastics Design Data*, British Standards Institution, London.
13. BS 3505: 1968, *Specification for Unplasticized PVC Pipe for Cold-Water Services*, British Standards Institution, London.
14. BS 3284: 1967, *Specification for Polythene Pipe (Type 50) for Cold-Water Services*, British Standards Institution, London.
15. A. I. Smith and D. Scott, *The Technical Basis of Steel Specifications*, National Engineering Laboratory Report, No. 248, Sept. 1966 (see Table 1, p. 23).
16. G. Menges, *Kunststoffe-Berater*, 25 (1969).
17. E. Gaube and G. Menges, 'Buckling and denting of thermoplastics, using rigid polyethylene as example', *Kunststoffe*, **58**, 153–158 (1968).
18. G. Menges and E. Gaube, 'Failure by buckling', *Modern Plastics*, **46**, 96–98, 102, 104, 108, 110 (1969).
19. E. Baer, J. R. Knox, T. J. Linton and R. E. Maier, 'Structural design of plastics', *SPE Journal*, **16**, 396–406 (1960).
20. K. Forbes, A. McGregor and S. Turner, 'Design of fluid storage tanks from polypropylene', *Brit. Chem. Engng.*, **15**, 1333–1336 (1970).
21. G. Diedrich and E. Gaube, 'Welding methods for rigid polyethylene pipe and sheet: creep rupture strength and long-term welding factors', *Kunststoffe*, **60**, 74–80 (1970).

22. G. Menges and H. Schmidt, 'Correlation of stress crazing with tensile creep behaviour in thermoplastics', *Plastics & Polymers*, **38**, 13–19 (1970).
23. K. V. Gotham, 'A formalized experimental approach to the fatigue of thermoplastics', *Plastics & Polymers*, **37**, 309–319 (1969).
23a. S. Turner, 'Mechanical properties of plastics', Paper A.2.3, International Symposium on *Application of Plastics in Building, Rotterdam*, 27–29 April, 1970.
24. W. F. Ratcliffe and S. Turner, 'Engineering design: data required for plastics materials', *Trans. J. Plast. Inst.*, **34**, 137–145 (1966).
25. D. McCammond, 'The substitution of time-dependent data into Hookean formulae', *Trans. J. Plast. Inst.*, **35**, 409–413 (1967).
26. J. Bax, 'Representation and application of viscoelastic data', *Kunststoffe*, **57**, 473–475 (1967).
27. D. McCammond and P. P. Benham, 'A study of design stress analysis procedures for thermoplastics products using time-dependent data', *Plastics & Polymers*, **37**, 475–483 (1969).
28. J. G. Williams, 'Limit analysis of plastics', *Trans. J. Plast. Inst.*, **34**, 123–125 (1966).
29. C. H. Weber, E. N. Robertson and W. F. Bartoe, 'Time and temperature dependent modulus concept for plastics', *Ind. Engng. & Chem.*, **47**, 1311–1316 (1955).
30. A. A. Macleod, 'Design of plastic structures for complex static stress systems', *Ind. Engng. & Chem.*, **47**, 1319–1323 (1955).
31. A. J. Donald and J. G. Williams, 'Designing with thermoplastics in bending', *Trans. J. Plast. Inst.*, **35**, 595–600 (1967).
32. L. Z. Salchev and J. G. Williams, 'Bending and buckling phenomena in thermoplastic beams', *Plastics & Polymers*, **37**, 159–163 (1969).
33. G. Watson, 'Designing beam springs in thermoplastics materials', *Trans. J. Plast. Inst.*, **33**, 109 (1965).
34. J. W. Schweiker and O. M. Sidebottom, 'Creep of thick-walled cylinders subjected to internal pressure and axial load', *Experimental Mechanics*, **5**, 186–192 (1965).
35. P. C. Powell, 'Prediction of long-term deformation in thermoplastics', *Progr. Plast.*, 73–4, 78, 81, 83, 86, 88, 91–2, 95 (1969).
36. C. Austin, 'Designing engineering components in plastics', *Rubber & Plastics Age*, **48**, 263, 265–6, 271 (1967).
37. R. M. Ogorkiewicz and A. A. M. Sayigh, 'Creep of sandwich beams in three-point bending', *Plastics & Polymers*, **37**, 15–20 (1969).
38. P. P. Benham and D. McCammond, 'Studies of creep and contraction rates in thermoplastics', *Plastics & Polymers*, **39**, 130–136 (1970).
39. S. Turner, 'The strain response of plastics to complex stress histories', *Poly. Engng. & Sci.*, **6**, 306–316 (1966).
40. S. Turner, 'Creep studies on plastics', *Applied Polymer Symposia No. 17*, Wiley, 1971, 213–240.
41. S. Turner, 'Creep of glassy polymers', in *The Physics of Glassy Polymers*, to be published by Applied Science Publishers Ltd.
42. P. C. Powell, 'Prediction of end-product performance: the present position', *Plastics & Polymers*, **39**, 43–52 (1971).
43. P. C. Powell and S. Turner, 'The transformation of research results into design practice', *Plastics & Polymers*, **39**, 261–265 (1971).
44. D. F. Oxley and D. J. H. Sandiford, 'Sandwich moulding', *Plastics & Polymers*, **39**, 288–292 (1971).
45. R. M. Ogorkiewicz and A. A. M. Sayigh, 'Deflection of polypropylene sandwich mouldings under bending', *Plastics & Polymers*, **40**, 59–64 (1972).

46. M. J. Bonnin, C. M. R. Dunn and S. Turner, 'A comparison of torsional and flexural deformation in plastics', *Plastics & Polymers*, **37**, 517–522 (1969).
47. R. M. Ogorkiewicz and S. Turner, 'Mechanical characteristics of reinforced plastics', *Plastics & Polymers*, **39**, 209–213 (1971).
48. M. Abrahams and J. Dimmock, 'Mechanical and economic comparisons of reinforced thermoplastics', *Plastics & Polymers*, **39**, 187–193 (1971).
49. O. Hahmann, P. Potthoff and H. Stumpf, 'Investigations into the use of high-density polyethylene for bottle crates', *Kunststoffe*, **54**, 291–296 (1964).
50. A. C. Morris and A. G. Whittal, 'Plastics Crates', *Plastics*, 1421–23, 1543, 1546–7 (1966); 82–85, 186–189 (1967).
51. G. Menges, H. Schulze and F. Knipschild, 'Design principles for calculating the size of rib reinforced sheets of thermoplastics materials', Berichte zum 6, Kunststofftechnischen Kolloquium des IKV in Aachen, 22 and 23 March 1972, 177–183.
52. A. G. H. Dietz, 'Plastics in load-bearing structures', *Plastics in Building Symposium*, Rotterdam 27–29, April, 1970.
53. K. V. Gotham, 'Long-term strength: the ductile–brittle transition in static fatigue', *Plastics & Polymers*, **40**, 59–64 (1972).
54. K. V. Gotham and S. Turner, 'The long-term strength of polyvinylchloride', SPE ANTEC, Chicago, May 1972.
55. H. Beuschel, 'The technological challenge of the next ten years', *Plastics & Polymers*, **38**, 395–403 (1970).
56. J. G. Williams, 'Theoretical design of plastics pipes', *Trans. J. Plast. Inst.*, **33**, 103–106 (1965).
57. A. van der Boogaart and C. E. Turner, 'Fracture mechanics: a review of principles with special reference to applications for glassy plastics in sheet form', *Trans. J. Plast. Inst.*, **31**, 109–117 (1963).
58. J. G. Williams, J. C. Radon and C. E. Turner, 'Designing against fracture in brittle plastics', *Poly. Engng. & Sci.*, **8**, 130–141 (1968).
59. E. H. Andrews, 'Fatigue in polymers', in *Testing of Polymers*, 4 (Ed. W. E. Brown), Interscience, 1969.
60. P. C. Paris and G. C. M. Sih, 'Stress analysis of cracks', in *Fracture toughness testing and its applications*, ASTM Special Technical Publication No. 381, 1965.
61. S. J. Hutchinson and P. P. Benham, 'Low-frequency plane-bending of PVC', *Plastics & Polymers*, **38**, 102–106 (1970).
62. G. P. Marshall, L. E. Culver and J. G. Williams, 'Environmental stress crack growth in low density polyethylene', *Plastics & Polymers*, **38**, 95–101 (1970).
63. P. G. Faulkner and J. R. Atkinson, 'The environmental stress cracking and crazing of PVC', *Plastics & Polymers*, **40**, 109–117 (1972).

Index